Everyday
Mathematics®

Home Links

TRINITY CHRISTIAN COLLEGE
PALOS HEIGHTS IL 60463
JENNIE HUIZENGA MEM LIB

DATE DUE

NOV 2 1 2004			
MAR 1 8 2005			
MAY 1 9 2006			
	MAR 2 9 2007		
NOV 2 5 2007			
OCT 2 2 2009			
AUG 1 0 2012			
	SEP 2 1 2012		

PRINTED IN U.S.A.

D1413227

Everyday Mathematics®

Home Links

**The University of Chicago
School Mathematics Project**

EVERYDAY
LEARNING

Chicago, Illinois

UCSMP Elementary Materials Component

Max Bell, Director

Authors

Max Bell
Jean Bell
John Bretzlauf*
Amy Dillard*
Robert Hartfield
Andy Isaacs*
James McBride, Director
Kathleen Pitvorec*
Peter Saecker

Technical Art

Diana Barrie*

Second Edition only

Everyday Learning Development Staff

Editorial: Anna Belluomini, Mary Cooney, Julie Crawford, Christine Fraser, Elizabeth Glosniak, Michael Murphy, Janet Kapche Razionale
Design: Fran Brown, Jess Schaal
Production: Hector Cuadra, Annette Davis, Tina Dunlap, Elizabeth Gabbard, Derek Wegmann

Additional Credits

Elizabeth Allen, Kathy Burke, Lindaanne Donohoe, Mary Ghislin, Susan Halko,
Herman Adler Design Group, Made in Chicago Design, Yoshi Miyake, Katie Telser,
Regina Thoeming

Photo Credits

Phil Martin/Photography, Jack Demuth/Photography, Cover Credits: Sand, starfish, orange wedges, crystal/Bill Burlingham Photography, Photo Collage: Herman Adler Design

Contributors

Carol Arkin, Robert Balfanz, Sharlean Brooks, Ellen Dairyko, James Flanders,
David Garcia, Rita Gronbach, Deborah Arron Leslie, Curtis Lieneck, Diana Marino,
Mary Moley, William D. Pattison, William Salvato, Jean Marie Sweigart, Leeann Wille

Permissions

page 125, Home Link 5.13, Ice cream cone by Jim Quinn/Chicago Tribune
page 125, Home Link 5.13, John Edwards/Tony Stone Images
page 127, Home Link 5.13, Soup can and ice cream cone by Jack Demuth/Photography

ISBN 1-57039-946-8

Copyright © 2001 by Everyday Learning Corporation. All rights reserved. Printed in the United States of America. Individual purchasers of this book are hereby granted the right to make sufficient copies of the reproducible masters in this book for use by all students in a single classroom. This permission is limited to a single classroom and does not apply to entire schools or school systems. Institutions purchasing the book should pass the permission on to a single classroom. Copying of this book or its parts for resale is prohibited.

Any questions regarding this policy should be addressed to:

Everyday Learning Corporation
P.O. Box 812960
Chicago, IL 60681
www.everydaylearning.com

1 2 3 4 5 6 7 8 9   VL   05 04 03 02 01 00

Contents

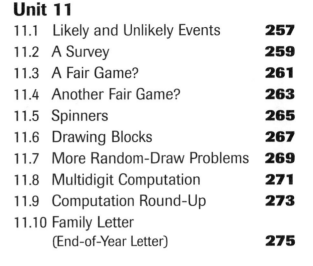

Family Letter

Introduction to Third Grade Everyday Mathematics

Welcome to *Third Grade Everyday Mathematics*. It is part of an elementary school mathematics curriculum developed by the University of Chicago School Mathematics Project. *Everyday Mathematics* offers children a broad background in mathematics.

Several features of the program are described below to help familiarize you with the structure and expectations of *Everyday Mathematics*.

A problem-solving approach based on everyday situations By making connections between their own knowledge and their experiences, both in school and outside of school, children learn basic math skills in meaningful contexts so that the mathematics becomes "real."

Frequent practice of basic skills Instead of practice presented in a single, tedious drill format, children practice basic skills in a variety of more engaging ways. In addition to completing daily review exercises covering a variety of topics, patterning on the number grid, and working with addition and subtraction fact families in different formats, children will play games that are specifically designed to develop basic skills.

An instructional approach that revisits concepts regularly To enhance the development of basic skills and concepts, children regularly revisit previously learned concepts and repeatedly practice skills encountered earlier. The lessons are designed to take advantage of previously learned concepts and skills and to build on them throughout the year instead of treating them as isolated bits of knowledge.

A curriculum that explores mathematical content beyond basic arithmetic Mathematics standards around the world indicate that basic arithmetic skills are only the beginning of the mathematical knowledge children will need as they develop critical thinking skills. In addition to basic arithmetic, *Everyday Mathematics* develops concepts and skills in the following topics—numeration; operations and computation; data and chance; geometry; measurement and reference frames; and patterns, functions, and algebra.

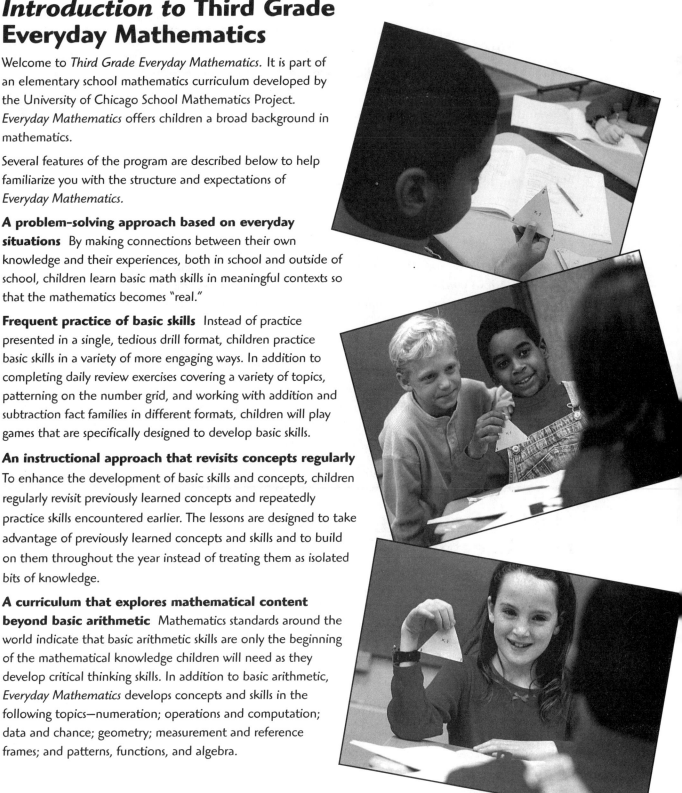

Third Grade Everyday Mathematics emphasizes the following content:

Numeration Counting patterns; place value; reading and writing whole numbers through 1,000,000; fractions, decimals, and integers

Operations and Computation Multiplication and division facts extended to multidigit problems; working with properties; operations with fractions and money

Data and Chance Collecting, organizing, and displaying data using tables, charts, and graphs

Geometry Exploring 2- and 3-dimensional shapes and other geometric concepts

Measurement Recording equivalent units of length; recognizing appropriate units of measure for various items; finding the areas of rectangles by counting squares

Reference Frames Using multiplication arrays, coordinate grids, thermometers, and map scales to estimate distances

Patterns, Functions, and Algebra Finding patterns on the number grid; solving Frames-and-Arrows puzzles having two rules; completing variations of "What's My Rule?" activities; exploring the relationship between multiplication and division; using parentheses in writing number models; naming missing parts of number models

Everyday Mathematics will provide you with ample opportunities to monitor your child's progress and to participate in your child's mathematics experiences.

Throughout the year, you will receive Family Letters to keep you informed of the mathematical content your child will be studying in each unit. Each letter will include a vocabulary list, suggested Do-Anytime Activities for you and your child, and an answer guide to selected Home Link (homework) activities.

You will enjoy seeing your child's confidence and comprehension soar as he or she connects mathematics to everyday life. We look forward to an exciting year!

Unit 1: Routines, Reviews, and Assessment

The first purpose of Unit 1 is to establish routines that children will use throughout the school year. The second purpose is to review and extend mathematical concepts that were developed in previous grades.

In Unit 1, children will look for examples of numbers for the Numbers All Around Museum. Examples of numbers might include identification numbers, measures, money, telephone numbers, addresses, and codes. Children will also look at number patterns in a problem-solving setting by using number-grid puzzles and Frames-and-Arrows diagrams. (See examples on the next page.)

Throughout Unit 1, children will use numbers within the context of real-life situations. After reviewing place-value concepts, children will work with money and pretend to purchase items from a vending machine and a store. The emphasis on applying numbers to the real world is also reflected in the yearlong Length-of-Day Project, a weekly routine that involves collecting, recording, and graphing sunrise/sunset data.

Vocabulary

Important terms in Unit 1:

digits The symbols from 0 through 9 that are used—sometimes in conjunction with other symbols—to record any number in our numbering system.

estimate The calculation of a close, rather than an exact, answer.

tool kits Individual zippered bags or boxes used in the classroom; they contain a variety of items, such as rulers, play money, and number cards, to help children understand mathematical ideas.

number grid A table in which numbers are arranged consecutively, usually in rows of 10. A move from one number to the next within a row is a change of 1; a move from one number to the next within a column is a change of 10.

									0
1	2	3	4	5	6	7	8	9	10
11	12	13	14	15	16	17	18	19	20
21	22	23	24	25	26	27	28	29	30

number-grid puzzle A piece of the number grid in which some, but not all, of the numbers are missing. Number-grid puzzles are used for reinforcing place-value concepts.

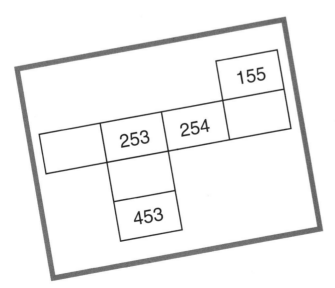

range The difference between the greatest and the least numbers in a set of data. In the set of data below, 9 is the range $(41 - 32 = 9)$.

$$32 \quad 33 \quad 35 \quad 35 \quad 36 \quad 40 \quad 41$$

mode The value that occurs most often in a set of data. In the set of data above, 35 is the mode.

name-collection box A boxlike diagram tagged with a given number and used for collecting equivalent names for that number.

300	
three hundred	$310 - 10$
$150 + 150$	$260 + 40$
	$300 - 0$

Frames and Arrows Diagrams that are used to represent number sequences, or sets of numbers that are ordered according to a rule. These problem-solving diagrams consist of frames connected by arrows to show the path from one frame to the next. Each frame contains a number in the sequence; each arrow represents a rule that determines which number goes in the next frame.

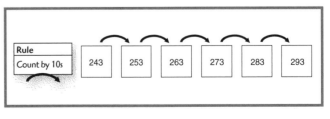

As You Help Your Child with Homework

As your child brings home assignments, you may want to go over the instructions together, clarifying them as necessary. The answers listed below will guide you through this unit's Home Links.

Home Link 1.2

2. 000800   **3.** 000810   **4.** 000910
5. 001910   **6.** 1,111 miles

Home Link 1.3

Sample answers:

1. ②,4̶8̶0̶   **2.** 2,560   **3.** 2,450
4. 100   **5.** 299   **6.** 990   **7.** 4,900

Home Link 1.4

2. 8:00   **3.** 3:30   **4.** 6:15   **5.** 11:45
6. 7:10   **7.** 5:40

Home Link 1.5

1.

Time Spent Watching TV	
Hours	Children
0	/
1	//
2	//
3	////
4	/
5	/

2. 0   **3.** 5   **4.** 5   **5.** 3

Home Link 1.6

1. **18** Sample answers:

10 + 5 + 3	double 9
9 − 1 + 10	eighteen
20 − 2	10 less than 28
H̶H̶T̶ H̶H̶T̶ H̶H̶T̶ ///	9 + 9

2. **12**

H̶H̶T̶H̶H̶T̶	one dozen
7 + 5	number of months in 1 year
15 − 3	10 + 2
18̶ ✗ 4̶	9̶ ✗ 3̶

Home Link 1.7

2. 154; 23   **3.** 148; 29   **4.** 169; 29
5. 22   **6.** 28

Home Link 1.11

1.
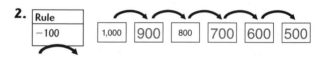
Rule +3¢ : 12¢ | 15¢ | 18¢ | 21¢ | 24¢ | 27¢

2.
Rule −100 : 1,000 | 900 | 800 | 700 | 600 | 500

4. $1.46   **5.** $0.87   **6.** $12.06

Home Link 1.12

1. a.   **b.**

2. a.   **b.**

3. a.   **b.**

4. 1 hour 35 min

Numbers All Around Museum

Family Note

In the *Third Grade Everyday Mathematics* program, children "do mathematics." We expect that children will want to share their enthusiasm for the mathematics activities they do in school with members of their families. Your child will bring home assignments and activities to do as homework throughout the year. These assignments, called "Home Links," will be identified by the symbol at the top of the page. The assignments will not take very much time to complete, but most of them involve interaction with an adult or an older child.

There are good reasons for including Home Links in the third grade program:
· The assignments encourage children to take initiative and responsibility for completing them. As you respond with encouragement and assistance, you help your child build independence and self-confidence.

· Home Links reinforce newly learned skills and concepts. They provide thinking and practice time at each child's own pace.

· These assignments are often designed to relate what is done in school to children's lives outside school. This helps tie mathematics to the real world, which is very important in the *Everyday Mathematics* program.

· The Home Links assignments will give you a better idea of the mathematics your child is learning in school.

Generally, you can help by listening and responding to your child's requests and comments about mathematics. You can help by linking numbers to real life; pointing out ways in which you use numbers (time, TV channels, page numbers, telephone numbers, bus routes, and so on). Extending the notion that "children who are read to, read," *Everyday Mathematics* supports the belief that children who have someone do math with them, will learn mathematics. Playful counting and thinking games are very helpful in promoting such learning.

The Family Note will explain what the children are learning in class. Use it to help you understand where the assignment fits into your child's learning.

Numbers All Around Museum (cont.) Home Link 1.1

Family Note

Numbers on advertisements show quantities and prices (3 cans of soup for $1.00); food containers show weight or capacity (a $15\frac{1}{2}$ oz can of black beans or 1 quart carton of milk); and telephone books show addresses and phone numbers. By helping your child find examples of numbers in everyday life, you will reinforce the idea that numbers are all around us and used for many reasons. Help your child recognize numbers by filling in the table.

Please return this Home Link to school within the next few days.

Find as many different kinds of numbers as you can. Record the numbers in the table below. Be sure to include the unit if there is one.

Number	Unit (if there is one)	Where you found the number
Example: 14	oz	cereal box

Find objects or pictures with numbers on them to bring to school.
Check with an adult at home first. Do not bring anything valuable.

Odometer Readings

Family Note

An *odometer* is an instrument for measuring the distance traveled by a vehicle. We ask children to look at an odometer because it is important that they see mathematics at work in the real world. The odometer problems below illustrate what happens to the digits in a number when the number is increased by 1, 10, 100, and 1,000.

Some odometers show tenths of a mile. You might discuss the fact that the tenths digit shows fractions of a mile and rotates relatively quickly.

Please return this Home Link to school tomorrow.

1. Ask someone at home to explain what an odometer is. If your family owns a car, draw a picture of an odometer on the back of this page. Show the number of miles that the car has been driven.

In each problem, write your answer in the odometer.

2. Jackie's odometer shows 799 miles.

   $\boxed{0\ 0\ 0\ 7\ 9\ 9}$

   Jackie drives 1 mile on a short trip. What does her odometer show at the end of the trip?

3. Jackie now drives 10 miles on a trip. What does the odometer show at the end of this trip?

   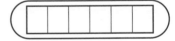

4. Jackie now drives 100 miles on a trip. What does the odometer show at the end of this trip?

   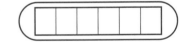

5. Jackie drives 1,000 miles on one more long trip. What does the odometer show at the end of this trip?

   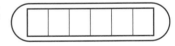

Challenge

6. How far did Jackie drive in all on the four trips? _____ miles

   On the back of the page, explain or show how you got your answer.

Place-Value Practice

Family Note

In the last lesson, children learned how to use a nmber grid and how to solve number-grid puzzles. The Challenge problems below give children more practice with what they have learned. For information about nmber grids and number-grid puzzles, see pages 6–9 in the *Student Reference Book*.

Please return this Home Link to school tomorrow.

1. Have someone at home tell you a 4-digit number to write down.

   a. Write the number. _____

   b. Circle the thousands place.

   c. Put an X through the tens place.

   d. Underline the ones place.

2. Write the number that is 100 more than your number in Problem 1.

   _____

3. Write the number that is 10 less than your number in Problem 1.

   _____

Solve.

4. 99 + 1 = _____

5. 300 – 1 = _____

6. 1,000 – 10 = _____

7. 5,000 – 100 = _____

Challenge

8.
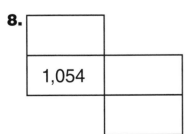

9.
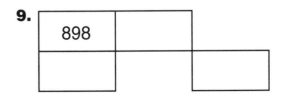

Telling Time

Family Note

Today we discussed some of the tools used in mathematics. We reviewed how to read a ruler to the nearest inch and nearest centimeter and how to read a clock face to tell time to the nearest half-hour, nearest quarter-hour, and nearest 5 minutes. Help your child read and write each time.

Please return this Home Link to school tomorrow.

1. Draw the hour hand and the minute hand to show the time right now. Write the time.

_____ : _____

Write the time shown.

2.

_____ : _____

3.

_____ : _____

4.

_____ : _____

5.

_____ : _____

6.

_____ : _____

7.

_____ : _____

8. Show someone at home how you solved the hardest problem on this page.

Name _____ Date _____ Time _____

How Much TV Did They Watch?

Home Link 1.5

Family Note

You can find information about tally charts on pages 70–72 in the *Student Reference Book.* You can find information about the minimum, maximum, range, and mode of a set of data on pages 73 and 75.

Please return this Home Link to school tomorrow.

Paul asked some of his classmates how many hours they watched television yesterday. His classmates reported the following numbers of hours:

| 1 hour | 3 hours | 1 hour | 5 hours | 0 hours | 2 hours |
| 4 hours | 3 hours | 2 hours | 3 hours | 3 hours | |

1. Make a tally chart for the data.

Time Spent Watching TV	
Hours	**Children**

2. What was the least (minimum) number of hours watched? _____ hours

3. What was the greatest (maximum) number of hours watched? _____ hours

4. What is the range for the data? _____ hours (Remember that *range* is the difference between the greatest number and the least number.)

5. What is the mode for the data? _____ hours

6. How many hours a day do you usually watch TV? _____ hours

Use with Lesson 1.5.

Name-Collection Boxes

Family Note

You can find an explanation of name-collection boxes on pages 14 and 15 in the *Student Reference Book*.

Please return this Home Link to school tomorrow.

SRB 14 15

1. Write at least 10 names for the number 18 in the name-collection box. Then explain to someone at home how the box works. Have that person add another name for 18.

18

2. Three of the names do not belong in this box. Cross them out. Then write the name of the box on the tag.

~~HHT HHT~~   one dozen
7 + 5   number of months in 1 year
15 − 3   10 + 2
18 − 4   9 − 3

3. Make up a problem like Problem 2. Choose a name for the box but do not write it on the tag. Write 4 names for the number and 2 names that are not names for the number.

To check if the problem makes sense, ask someone at home to tell you which 2 names do not belong in the box. Have that person write the name of the box on the tag.

Finding Differences

Family Note

It is not expected that your child knows how to use a traditional method of subtraction to solve these problems. Formal methods will be covered in the next unit. You can find an explanation of how to find differences on a number grid on page 8 in the *Student Reference Book*.

Please return this Home Link to school tomorrow.

1. Fill in the numbers on the number grid below.

	132								
									150
		154							
					177				

Use the number grid above to help you answer the following questions.

2. Which is more, 154 or 131? _____   How much more? _____

3. Which is less, 177 or 148? _____   How much less? _____

4. Which is more, 140 or 169? _____   How much more? _____

5. The difference between 180 and 158 is _____.

6. The difference between 170 and 142 is _____.

Challenge

7. Explain how you found your answer in Problem 5.

_____

_____

Large and Small Numbers

Family Note

We have been reviewing place–value concepts using large and small numbers in this lesson. For more information about place value, see pages 18 and 19 in the *Student Reference Book.*

Please return this Home Link to school tomorrow.

SRB
18 19

You will need a die or a deck of cards numbered from 0 to 9.

1. Roll a die 4 times (or draw 4 cards).

   a. Record the digit for each roll (or each card) in a blank.

   _____ _____ _____ _____

   b. Make the largest 4-digit number you can using these digits.

   _____ , _____ _____ _____

   c. Make the smallest 4-digit number you can using these digits. The number may not begin with a zero.

   _____ , _____ _____ _____

   d. Add the two numbers using a calculator. _____

   e. Find the difference between the two numbers. _____

2. Roll a die 5 times (or draw 5 cards).

   a. Record the digit for each roll (or each card) in a blank.

   _____ _____ _____ _____ _____

   b. Make the largest 5-digit number you can using these digits.

   _____ _____ , _____ _____ _____

   c. Make the smallest 5-digit number you can using these digits. The number may not begin with a zero.

   _____ _____ , _____ _____ _____

   d. Add the two numbers using a calculator. _____

   e. Find the difference between the two numbers. _____

Ad Hunt

Family Note

The children have been working on dollars-and-cents notation. Help your child locate ads that clearly show prices.

Please return this Home Link to school tomorrow.

1. Cut out four small advertisements from newspapers and magazines. Each ad must show the price of an item.

2. Put the ads in order from the least expensive item to the most expensive item.

3. Tape or glue your four ads in order on this page.

4. Bring extra ads to school to add to the Numbers All Around Museum.

Shopping in the Newspaper

Family Note

In this activity, your child will be looking for at least 5 different items to buy with $100. If there is money left over, your child can find something more to buy. If your child buys something in quantity (for example, 4 CDs), list each item and price on a separate line.

Please return this Home Link to school tomorrow.

Pretend that you have $100 to spend. Have someone at home help you find ads for at least 5 different items that you can buy. List the items and their prices below. DO NOT CALCULATE your total. Instead, estimate the total. You do not need to spend exactly $100.

Item	Price

Explain to someone at home how you estimated the total.

Frames and Arrows

 Family Note

You can find information about Frames-and-Arrows diagrams on pages 176 and 177 in the *Student Reference Book*.

Please return this Home Link to school tomorrow.

 SRB 176 177

Show someone at home how to complete these Frames-and-Arrows diagrams.

1.

Rule
+3¢

12¢ [ ] [ ] [ ] 24¢ [ ]

2.

Rule
−100

1,000 [ ] 800 [ ] [ ] [ ]

3.

Rule

24 ( ) ( ) 42 48 ( )

Review

Write each amount in dollars-and-cents notation.

4. $1 Q D N N P = $_____

5. D D Q N P D Q P = $_____

6. $10 $1 $1 N P = $_____

7. Draw coins to show $0.89 in at least two different ways.

Time Practice

Family Note

Your child has been learning about elapsed time in this lesson.

Please return this Home Link to school tomorrow.

Pretend you are setting your watch. Draw the hour hand and minute hand on the clock face to show the time.

1. a. Show a quarter to 6.

b. Show the time 2 hours and 15 minutes later.

2. a. Show half-past 8.

b. Show the time 4 hours and 20 minutes earlier.

3. a. Show 25 minutes past 11.

b. Show the time 3 hours and 40 minutes later.

4. Hilary and Jack started to work on a collage at 4:35. They finished it at

6:10. How long did it take them to make it? _____

Family Letter

Unit 2: Adding and Subtracting Whole Numbers

Unit 2 will focus on addition and subtraction of whole numbers, emphasizing problem-solving strategies and computational skills. In *Second Grade Everyday Mathematics,* children used shortcuts, fact families, Fact Triangles, and games to help them learn basic addition and subtraction facts. Such devices will continue to be used in third grade. Knowing the basic facts and their extensions is advantageous. Knowing that $6 + 8 = 14$, for example, makes it easy to solve such problems as $56 + 8 = ?$ and $60 + 80 = ?$ Later, knowing that $5 \times 6 = 30$ will make it easy to solve $5 \times 60 = ?$, $50 \times 60 = ?$, and so on.

In Unit 2, children will learn new methods for solving addition and subtraction problems. *Everyday Mathematics* encourages children to choose from any of these methods or to invent their own computation methods. When children create—and share—their own ways of doing operations instead of simply learning one method, they begin to realize that any problem can be solved in more than one way. They are more willing and able to take risks, think logically, and reason analytically.

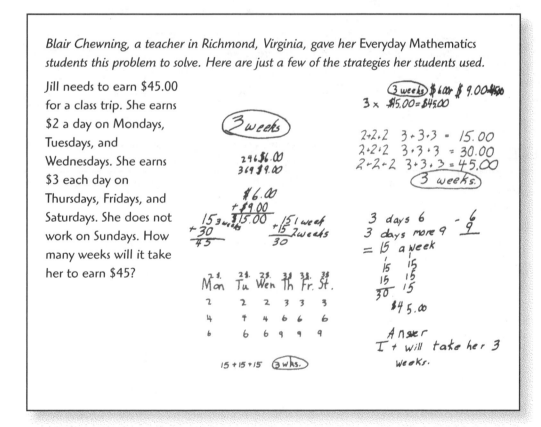

Blair Chewning, a teacher in Richmond, Virginia, gave her Everyday Mathematics *students this problem to solve. Here are just a few of the strategies her students used.*

Jill needs to earn $45.00 for a class trip. She earns $2 a day on Mondays, Tuesdays, and Wednesdays. She earns $3 each day on Thursdays, Fridays, and Saturdays. She does not work on Sundays. How many weeks will it take her to earn $45?

Finally, Unit 2 introduces another yearlong project—the National High/Low Temperatures Project. Children will calculate, record, and graph differences in temperatures from cities around the United States.

Math Tools

Your child will be using **Fact Triangles** to practice and review addition and subtraction facts. Fact Triangles are a "new and improved" version of flash cards; the addition and subtraction facts shown are made from the same three numbers, and this helps your child understand the relationships among those facts.

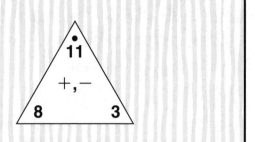

Vocabulary

Important terms in Unit 2:

fact family A collection of related addition and subtraction facts, or multiplication and division facts, made from the same numbers.

$$3 + 8 = 11$$
$$8 + 3 = 11$$
$$11 - 3 = 8$$
$$11 - 8 = 3$$

function machine An imaginary machine that processes numbers according to a certain rule. A number (input) is put into the machine and is transformed into a second number (output) through the application of the rule.

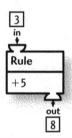

"What's My Rule?" table A list of number pairs in which the numbers in each pair are related to each other according to the same rule. Sometimes the rule and one number in each pair are given, and the other number is to be found. Sometimes the pairs are given and the rule is to be found.

in	out
3	8
5	10
8	13
10	15
16	21

number family A collection of addition and subtraction sentences, or multiplication and division sentences, made from the same three multidigit numbers.

$$221 + 229 = 450 \qquad 450 - 221 = 229$$
$$229 + 221 = 450 \qquad 450 - 229 = 221$$

number model A number sentence that shows how the parts of a number story are related. For example, $5 + 8 = 13$ shows how the parts are related in this number story: *5 children skating. 8 children playing ball. How many children in all?*

parts-and-total diagram A diagram used to represent problems in which two or more quantities are combined to form a total quantity. It is often used when the parts are known and the total is unknown. It can also be used when the total and one or more parts are known, but one part is unknown.

For example, the parts-and-total diagram here represents this number story: *Leo baked 24 cookies. Nina baked 26 cookies. How many cookies in all?*

Total	
50	
Part	Part
24	26

change diagram A diagram used to represent addition or subtraction problems in which a given quantity is increased or decreased. The diagram includes the starting quantity, the ending quantity, and the amount of the change.

For example, the change diagram here represents this subtraction problem: *Rita had $28 in her wallet. She spent $12 at the store. How much money is in Rita's wallet now?*

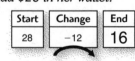

Start	Change	End
28	−12	16

comparison diagram A diagram used to represent problems in which two quantities are given and then compared to find how much more or less one quantity is than the other.

For example, the comparison diagram here represents this problem: *34 children ride the bus to school. 12 children walk to school. How many more children ride the bus?*

Quantity	
34	
Quantity	Difference
12	22

Use with Lesson 1.13.

Do-Anytime Activities

To work with your child on the concepts taught in this unit and in the previous unit, try these interesting and rewarding activities:

1 Review addition and subtraction facts. Make $+,-$ Fact Triangles for facts that your child needs to practice.

2 Practice addition and subtraction fact extensions. *For example:*

$$6 + 7 = 13 \qquad\qquad 13 - 7 = 6$$

$$60 + 70 = 130 \qquad\qquad 23 - 7 = 16$$

$$600 + 700 = 1,300 \qquad\qquad 83 - 7 = 76$$

3 When your child adds or subtracts multidigit numbers, talk about the strategy that works best. Try not to impose the strategy that works best for you! Here are some problems to try:

$267 + 743 =$ _____

$794 - 554 =$ _____

_____ $= 851 + 697$

$840 - 694 =$ _____

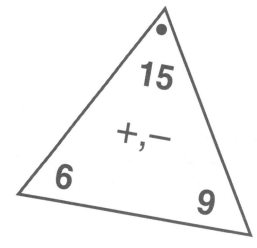

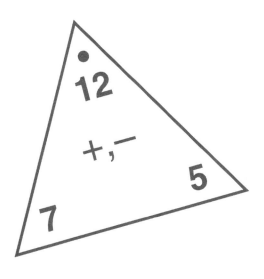

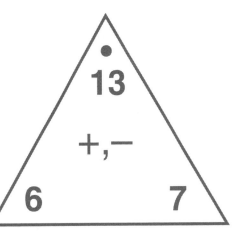

As You Help Your Child with Homework

As your child brings home assignments, you may want to go over the instructions together, clarifying them as necessary. The answers listed below will guide you through this unit's Home Links.

Home Link 2.1

1. $9 + 6 = 15$; $6 + 9 = 15$; $15 - 9 = 6$; $15 - 6 = 9$

2. $25 + 50 = 75$; $50 + 25 = 75$; $75 - 25 = 50$; $75 - 50 = 25$

Home Link 2.2

1. 16; 26; 76; 106   **2.** 12; 22; 62; 282

3. 8; 28; 58; 98   **4.** 5; 15; 115; 475

5. 13; 130; 1,300; 13,000

Home Link 2.3

1.

in	out
14	7
7	0
12	5
15	8
10	3
21	14

2.

in	out
7	16
9	18
37	46
77	86
49	58

Answers vary.

3.

in

Rule

Add 30

out

in	out
70	100
20	50
30	60
90	120
50	80

Answers vary.

Home Link 2.4

1. 55 minutes; $25 + 30 = 55$

2. 39 shells; $23 + 16 = 39$

3. 700 cans; $300 + 400 = 700$

Home Link 2.5

1. $9; $25 - 16 = 9$ or $16 + 9 = 25$

2. $49; $35 + 14 = 49$

Home Link 2.6

1. $30; $43 - 13 = 30$ or $13 + 30 = 43$

2. 9 days; $28 - 19 = 9$ or $19 + 9 = 28$

3. 15 children; $40 - 25 = 15$

Home Link 2.7

1. 337   **2.** 339   **3.** 562

4. 574   **5.** 627   **6.** 1,214

Home Link 2.8

1. 202   **2.** 122   **3.** 206

4. 439   **5.** 487

Home Link 2.9

1. 38   **2.** 213   **3.** 40

4. 70   **5.** 915   **6.** 55 blocks

7. 19 pages

Use with Lesson 1.13.

Fact Families and Number Families

Family Note

Work on fact and number families by focusing on related addition and subtraction facts. For example, 7 + 5 = 12, 5 + 7 = 12, 12 − 7 = 5, and 12 − 5 = 7.

Please return this Home Link to school tomorrow.

Show someone at home how to use a Fact Triangle.

1. Write the fact family for the numbers 9, 6, and 15. Write two addition and two subtraction facts.

_____ _____

_____ _____

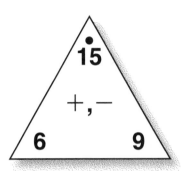

2. Write the number family for 25, 50, and 75.

_____ _____

_____ _____

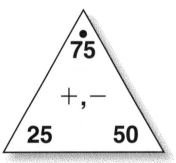

Make up one more fact family and one more number family. Write them below.

3. _____ _____

_____ _____

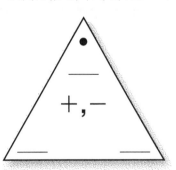

4. _____ _____

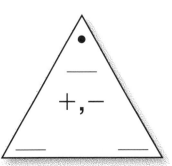

Addition/Subtraction Fact Extensions Home Link 2.2

Family Note

Knowing basic facts, such as $6 + 7 = 13$, makes it easy to solve similar problems with larger numbers, such as $60 + 70 = 130$. Help your child think of more fact extensions to complete this Home Link.

Please return this Home Link to school tomorrow.

Write the answer for each problem.

1. I know: 9
$+ 7$ This helps me know: 19
$+ 7$ 69
$+ 7$ 99
$+ 7$

2. I know: 8
$+ 4$ This helps me know: 18
$+ 4$ 58
$+ 4$ 278
$+ \;\; 4$

3. I know: 15
$- 7$ This helps me know: 35
$- 7$ 65
$- 7$ 105
$- \;\; 7$

4. I know: 13
$- 8$ This helps me know: 23
$- 8$ 123
$- \;\; 8$ 483
$- \;\; 8$

5. I know: 6
$+ 7$ This helps me know: 60
$+ 70$ 600
$+ 700$ 6,000
$+ 7,000$

Make up another set of fact extensions.

6. I know: This helps me know:

"What's My Rule?"

Family Note

You can find an explanation of function machines and "What's My Rule?" tables on pages 178–180 in the *Student Reference Book*. Help your child fill in all the missing parts for these problems.

Please return this Home Link to school tomorrow.

SRB 178–180

Practice facts and fact extensions. Complete the "What's My Rule?" problems. Create problems of your own for the last table.

1.

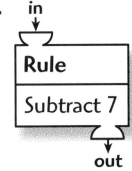

in → Rule **Subtract 7** → out

in	out
14	
	0
12	
	8
	3
21	

2.

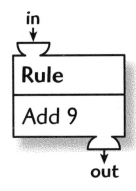

in → Rule **Add 9** → out

in	out
7	
	18
37	
	86
49	

3.

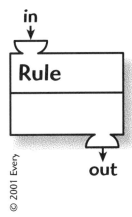

in → Rule → out

in	out
70	100
20	
	60
90	120
50	

4.

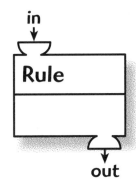

in → Rule → out

in	out

© 2001 Every

Parts-and-Total Number Stories

**Home Link
2.4**

**Family
Note**

Today your child learned about a diagram that helps organize the information in a number story. We call it a *parts-and-total diagram*. For more information, see pages 188 and 189 in the *Student Reference Book*.

Please return this Home Link to school tomorrow.

SRB
188 189

For each problem, write the numbers you know in the parts-and-total diagram. Write ? for the number you want to find. Then solve the problem. Write the answer and a number model. Tell someone at home how you know that each answer makes sense.

1. Marisa read her book for 25 minutes on Monday and 30 minutes on Tuesday. That was how many minutes in all?

Answer the question: _____
                                (unit)

Number model: _____

Total	
Part	**Part**

2. Liz has 23 shells in her collection, and Chris has 16 shells. What is the total number of shells?

Answer the question: _____
                                (unit)

Number model: _____

Total	
Part	**Part**

3. The second graders collected 300 cans to recycle. The third graders collected 400 cans. What was the total number of cans they collected?

Answer the question: _____
                                (unit)

Number model: _____

Total	
Part	**Part**

Change Number Stories

Family Note

Today your child learned about another diagram that helps organize the information in a number story. It is called a *change diagram.* For more information, see pages 186 and 187 in the *Student Reference Book.*

Please return this Home Link to school tomorrow.

SRB
186 187

For each number story, write the numbers you know in the change diagram. Write ? for the number you want to find. Then solve the problem. Write the answer and a number model.

Also, tell someone at home how you know that each answer makes sense.

1. Marcus had $25 in his wallet. He spent $16 at the store. How much money was in Marcus's wallet then?

Start	Change	End

Answer the question: _____
(unit)

Number model: _____

2. Jasmine had $35. She earned $14 mowing lawns. How much money did she have then?

Start	Change	End

Answer the question: _____
(unit)

Number model: _____

3. Make up your own change-to-more or change-to-less number story.

_____

_____

Answer the question: _____
(unit)

Start	Change	End

Number model: _____

Comparison Number Stories

Family Note

Today your child learned about a *comparison diagram*. It helps organize information in a number story. To read more, see page 190 in the *Student Reference Book*.

Please return this Home Link to school tomorrow.

SRB
190

Write the numbers you know in the diagram. Write ? for the number you want to find. Then solve. Write the answer and a number model. Tell someone at home how you know that your answers make sense.

1. Jenna has $43. Her brother has $13. How much more money does Jenna have?

Answer the question: _____
(unit)

Number model: _____

Quantity

Quantity	Difference

2. There are 28 days until Pat's birthday and 19 days until José's birthday. How many more days does Pat have to wait?

Answer the question: _____
(unit)

Number model: _____

Quantity

Quantity	Difference

3. There are 25 children in the soccer club and 40 children in the science club. How many fewer children are in the soccer club?

Answer the question: _____
(unit)

Number model: _____

Quantity

Quantity	Difference

Addition: The Partial-Sums Method

Family Note

Today your child learned about adding two 3-digit numbers using a procedure called the *partial-sums method.* Your child may choose to use this method or may prefer a different procedure. For more information, see pages 51 and 52 in the *Student Reference Book.*

Please return this Home Link to school tomorrow.

SRB
51 52

Solve each addition problem. You might want to use the partial-sums method. Use a ballpark estimate to check that your answer makes sense. Write a number model to show your estimate.

1. 100s 10s 1s
    2 4 5
 +   9 2
 	
Ballpark estimate:
 	
_____
	2.
	     1 2 4
	 + 2 1 5
	
	Ballpark estimate:
	
	_____
		3.
		     2 4 5
		 + 3 1 7
		
		Ballpark estimate:
		
		_____

4.
     3 6 6
 + 2 0 8
 	
Ballpark estimate:
	5.
	     4 5 9
	 + 1 6 8
	
	Ballpark estimate:
		6.
		     7 6 9
		 + 4 4 5
		
		Ballpark estimate:

Subtraction: The Trade-First Method

Family Note

Today your child learned about subtracting two 3-digit numbers using the *trade-first method*. This method is similar to the traditional subtraction method that you probably know. However, the "regrouping" is done *before* the problem is solved—thus, the name "trade-first." For more information, see pages 54 and 55 in the *Student Reference Book*.

Please return this Home Link to school tomorrow.

SRB
54   55

Solve. You might want to use the trade-first method. Use a ballpark estimate to check that your answer makes sense. Write a number model.

Example	**1.**	**2.**
100s 10s 1s 3 16 4̸ 6̸ 8 − 2 7 4 1 9 4	531 − 329	331 − 209
Ballpark estimate: _____	Ballpark estimate: _____	Ballpark estimate: _____
3. 653 − 447	**4.** 925 − 486	**5.** 724 − 237
Ballpark estimate: _____	Ballpark estimate: _____	Ballpark estimate: _____

Three or More Addends

Family Note

This Home Link provides practice in looking for combinations that make addition easier. Guide your child to look for combinations that add up to 10, 20, 30, 40 and so on. Then add the rest of the numbers.

Please return this Home Link to school tomorrow.

Remember that when you add:

• The numbers can be in any order.

• Some combinations make the addition easier.

Add. Write the numbers in the order you added them. Tell someone at home why you added the numbers in that order.

Example	**1.** 6 + 18 + 14 = _____
5 + 17 + 25 + 3 = <u>50</u> I added in this order: $5 + 25 + 17 + 3$	I added in this order: _____
2. 125 + 13 + 75 = _____ I added in this order: _____	**3.** 15 + 6 + 14 + 5 = _____ I added in this order: _____
4. 33 + 22 + 8 + 7 = _____ I added in this order: _____	**5.** 150 + 215 + 300 + 50 + 200 = _____ I added in this order: _____ _____

Three or More Addends (cont.)

Solve these number stories.

6. Nico's baby brother has a basket of wooden blocks. 18 blocks are red, 15 are blue, and 22 are yellow. How many red, blue, and yellow blocks are in the basket?

Answer the question: _____ blocks

Number model: _____

Total		
Part	**Part**	**Part**

7. Marianna has 3 days to read a 58-page book. She read 17 pages on Monday and 22 pages on Tuesday. How many more pages does she need to read to finish the book?

Answer the question: _____ pages

Number model: _____

Total		
Part	**Part**	**Part**

8. Make up a number story with 4 or more addends.

_____

_____

_____

_____

_____

Answer the question: _____

(unit)

Number model: _____

Check: Does my answer make sense?

Family Letter

Unit 3: Linear Measures and Area

In Unit 3, children will develop their measurement sense by measuring lengths with standard units—in both the **U.S. customary system** and the **metric system.**

Children will practice reading a ruler to the nearest inch, nearest $\frac{1}{2}$ inch, nearest $\frac{1}{4}$ inch, and nearest centimeter as they measure a variety of objects, including parts of their own bodies, such as their hand spans, wrists, necks, and heights. In addition to the inch and centimeter, children will also measure with other standard units, such as the foot, yard, and meter. Children will begin to use certain body measures or the lengths of some everyday objects as **personal references** to estimate the lengths of other objects or distances. For example, a sheet of notebook paper that is about 1 foot long can help children estimate the length of a room in feet.

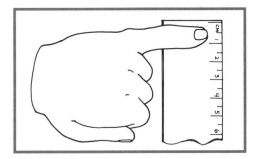

The width of my little finger is about one centimeter.

The concept of **perimeter** is also investigated in this unit. Children will use straws and twist-ties to build **polygons,** or 2-dimensional figures having connected sides. Then children will measure the distance around each polygon to find the perimeter.

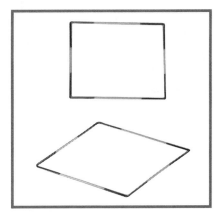

Children will also discover the meaning of **area** by "tiling" small rectangles with blocks and counting how many blocks cover the rectangles. Children see how to calculate area by tiling larger surfaces, such as tabletops and floors, with square feet and square yards.

In the last part of this unit, children will explore the **circumference** and **diameter** of circles. They will learn the "about 3 times" rule—that the circumference of a circle is a little more than 3 times the length of its diameter.

Please keep this Family Letter for reference as your child works through Unit 3.

Vocabulary

Important terms in Unit 3:

standard unit An agreed-upon unit of measure. *Examples:* foot, pound, gallon, meter, kilogram, liter.

length The measure of the distance between two points.

U.S. customary system The system of measurement that uses inches, feet, yards, and miles for measuring length.

metric system The system of measurement that uses millimeters, centimeters, meters, and kilometers for measuring length.

personal references Objects or distances that measure about 1 unit (inch, foot, yard, or mile; millimeter, centimeter, meter, or kilometer).

perimeter The distance around a surface that has a boundary.

circumference The distance around a circle; often thought of as the perimeter of a circle.

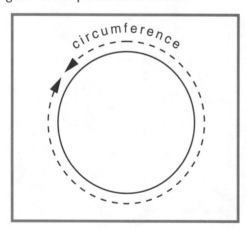

diameter The distance across the center of a circle.

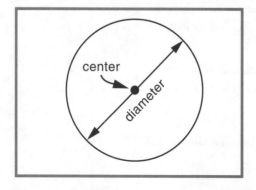

"about 3 times" circle rule The circumference of a circle is a little more than 3 times the length of its diameter.

polygon A 2-dimensional figure whose sides are line segments connected end to end. *Examples:* triangles, squares, rectangles, trapezoids.

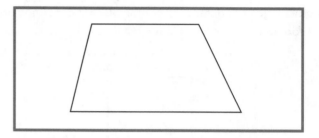

tiling The covering of a surface with shapes so that there are no gaps or overlaps, except for possible space around the edges.

area The number of units, usually squares, that can fit into a bounded surface.

standard square unit A unit used to measure area; a square that measures 1 inch, 1 centimeter, 1 yard, or 1 other standard measure of length on each side.

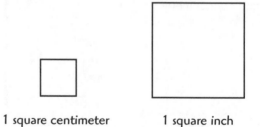

1 square centimeter   1 square inch

Use with Lesson 2.10.

Do-Anytime Activities

To work with your child on the concepts taught in this unit and in previous units, try these interesting and rewarding activities:

1 Encourage your child to find some personal references for making several measurements of length at home.

2 Practice using the personal references by *estimating* some lengths, and then practice using a ruler by *measuring* the actual lengths.

3 Practice finding perimeters of objects and circumferences of circular objects around your home.

As You Help Your Child with Homework

As your child brings home assignments, you may want to go over the instructions together, clarifying them as necessary. The answers listed below will guide you through this unit's Home Links.

Home Link 3.4

2. perimeter of polygon A = 20 cm

perimeter of polygon B = 20 cm

3. a. 12 ft   **3. b.** 60 in.

Home Link 3.6

1. Area = 24 square units   **2.** Area = 27 square units

Sample answer: Sample answer:

3. This is a 2-by-6 rectangle. Area = 12 square units

4. This is a 5-by-4 rectangle. Area = 20 square units

5. This is a 4-by-9 rectangle. Area = 36 square units

Home Link 3.7

1. 80 tiles   **2.** $160

3.   **4.** 30 plants

Building Skills through Games

In Unit 3, your child will practice addition and money skills by playing the following games. For detailed instructions, see the *Student Reference Book.*

Addition Top-It

Each player turns over two cards and calls out their sum. The player with the higher sum then takes all the cards from that round.

Beat the Calculator

A "Calculator" (a player who uses a calculator) and a "Brain" (a player who solves the problem without a calculator) race to see who will be first to solve addition problems.

Name That Number

Players turn over a card to find a number they must rename using any combination of five faceup cards.

4	10	8	12	2		6
4	10	8	12	2		6

The number 6 may be renamed as $4 + 2$, $8 - 2$, or $10 - 4$.

Name _____ Date _____ Time _____

Family Note

Help your child find labels, pictures, and descriptions that contain measurements. If possible, collect them in an envelope or folder so that your child can bring them to school tomorrow, along with this Home Link.

Please return this Home Link to school tomorrow.

1. Find items with measurements on them. Look at boxes and cans. List the items and their measurements.

Item	Measurement
milk carton	*1 quart*

2. Find pictures and ads that show measurements. Look in newspapers, magazines, or catalogs. Ask an adult if you can bring some of these to school.

3. If you do not understand the pictures that you found, ask someone at home to explain them to you. Be ready to talk about the examples at school.

Body Measures

Family Note

Help your child measure an adult at home. Use a tape measure if you can. Or use a piece of string. Mark lengths on the string with a pen, and then measure the string with a ruler.

Please return this Home Link to school tomorrow.

Measure an adult at home. Fill in the information below.

Name of adult: _____

Height: about _____ inches

Length of shoe: about _____ inches

Around neck: about _____ inches

Around wrist: about _____ inches

Distance from waist to floor: about _____ inches

Forearm: about	Hand span: about	Arm span: about
_____ inches	_____ inches	_____ inches
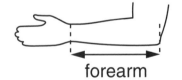 forearm	hand span	 ←arm span→

Reminder

Find more things with measurements on them. If you can, bring them to school. (Ask an adult first.) Or, write descriptions of them.

Measuring Height

Family Note

Measuring the height of the ceiling is easiest with such tools as a yardstick, a carpenter's ruler, or a metal tape measure. Another way is to attach a string to the handle of a broom and raise it to the ceiling. Have the string extend from the ceiling to the floor, cut the string to that length, and then measure the string with a ruler.

Please return this Home Link to school tomorrow.

Work with someone at home.

1. Measure the height of the ceiling in your room.

   The ceiling in my room is about _____ feet high.

2. Measure the height of a table.

   The table is between _____ and _____ feet high.

3. About how many tables could you stack in your room, one on top of the other?

   about _____ tables

4. Draw a picture of how the tables might look stacked in your room.

Perimeter

Family Note

The perimeter of a geometric figure is the distance around the figure. If the figure is a polygon, like those on this page, the perimeter can be found by adding the lengths of the sides. If you want to review this topic in detail with your child, use the *Student Reference Book*, pages 132 and 133.

Please return this Home Link to school tomorrow.

SRB 132 133

---

1. Estimate: Which has the larger perimeter, polygon A or polygon B? _____

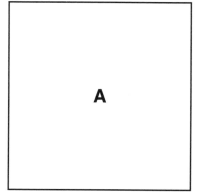

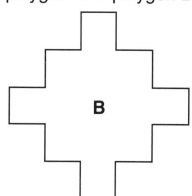

2. Check your estimate by measuring the perimeter of each polygon in centimeters. If you don't have a centimeter ruler, cut out the one at the bottom of the page.

perimeter of polygon A = _____ cm   perimeter of polygon B = _____ cm

3. What is the perimeter of each figure below?

a.

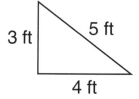

b. each side 10 inches

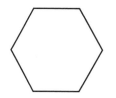

perimeter = _____ ft   perimeter = _____ in.

| 0 | 1 | 2 | 3 | 4 | 5 | 6 | 7 | 8 | 9 | 10 | 11 | 12 | 13 | 14 | 15 |

cm

Room Perimeters

Family Note

A personal measurement reference is something you know the measure of—for example, your height, or how many ounces in a soft-drink can. Personal references can help you estimate measures that you don't know. A person's pace can be defined as the length of a step, measured from heel to heel or from toe to toe. If you want, you may read about Personal Measurement References on pages 123, 124, 130, and 131 in the *Student Reference Book* with your child.

Please return this Home Link to school tomorrow.

Your pace is the length of one of your steps.

1. Find the perimeter, in paces, of your bedroom.

   Walk along each side and count the number of paces.

   The perimeter of my bedroom is about _____ paces.

2. Decide which room in your home has the largest perimeter.

   The _____ has the largest perimeter.

   Its perimeter is about _____ paces.

3. Draw this room below. Plan to share your drawing with the class.

Areas of Rectangles

Family Note

Today we discussed the concept of area. Area is a measure of the amount of surface inside a 2–dimensional shape. One way to find area is by counting same-size units inside a shape. For more information, see pages 136–138 in the *Student Reference Book.* In the next lesson, we will look at ways to calculate area.

Please return this Home Link to school tomorrow.

SRB
136–138

Show someone at home how to find the area of each rectangle. Make a dot in each square as you count the squares inside the rectangle.

1. Draw a 4-by-6 rectangle on the grid.

2. Draw a 3-by-9 rectangle.

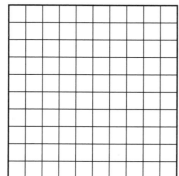 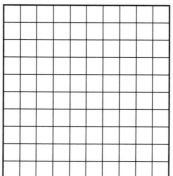

Fill in the blanks.

3.

This is a _____-by-_____ rectangle.

Area = _____ square units

4.

This is a _____-by-_____ rectangle.

Area = _____ square units

5.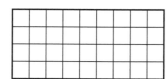

This is a _____-by-_____ rectangle.

Area = _____ square units

Area

> **Family Note**
>
> Today we discussed area as an array, or diagram. An array is a rectangular arrangement of objects in rows and columns. Help your child draw an array of the tomato plants in Problem 3. Use that diagram to find the total number of plants.
>
> *Please return this Home Link to school tomorrow.*

Mr. Li tiled his kitchen floor. This is what the tiled floor looks like.

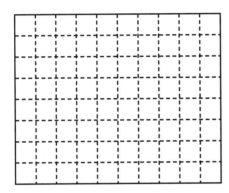

1. How many tiles did he use? _____ tiles

2. Each tile cost $2. How much did all the tiles cost? $_____

3. Mrs. Li planted tomato plants in her garden. She planted 5 rows with 6 plants in each row. Draw a diagram of the tomato plants. (*Hint:* You can show each plant with a large dot or an X.)

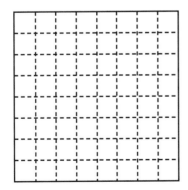

4. How many tomato plants are there in all? _____ plants

Circumference and Diameter

Family Note

Today in school your child learned the definitions of circumference and diameter. Ask your child to explain them to you. Help your child find and measure circular objects, such as cups, plates, clocks, cans, and so on. The "about 3 times" circle rule says that the circumference of any circle, no matter what size, is about 3 times its diameter. You might wish to review pages 134 and 135 in the *Student Reference Book* with your child.

Please return this Home Link to school tomorrow.

SRB
134 135

Measure the diameters and circumferences of circular objects at home. Use a tape measure if you have one. Or use a piece of string. Mark lengths on the string with your finger or a pen, and then measure the string.

Does the "about 3 times" circle rule seem to work? Share the "about 3 times" rule with someone at home.

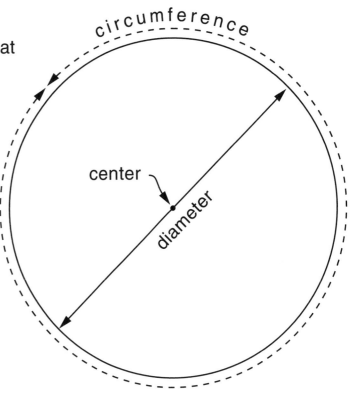

Diameter = 10 cm

Circumference = about 30 cm

Object	Diameter	Circumference

Family Letter

Unit 4: **Multiplication and Division**

Unit 4 focuses on the most common uses of multiplication and division—problems that involve equal sharing and equal grouping. In *Second Grade Everyday Mathematics,* children were exposed to multiplication and division number stories and multiplication and division facts. To solve multiplication and division number stories, children will refer to familiar strategies introduced in second grade:

- **Acting out problems using concrete objects, such as counters** (below)

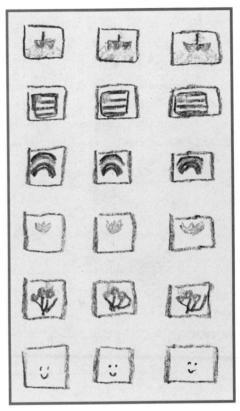

- **Representing problems with pictures and arrays** (right)

children	pennies per child	total number of pennies
4	?	28

A sheet of stamps has 6 rows. Each row has 3 stamps. How many stamps are on a sheet?

$6 \times 3 = 18$

- **Using diagrams to sort out quantities** (above)

Problem:	**Solution strategies:**
Each child has 2 apples. There are 16 apples. How many children have apples?	$2 \times ? = 16$, or I know that $16 \div 2 = 8$. If there are 16 apples and each child has 2, then there must be 8 children.

- **Using number models to represent solution strategies** (above)

Vocabulary

Important terms in Unit 4:

multiples Repeated groups of the same amount or number. Multiples of a number are the products of that number times other whole numbers. For example, the numbers 2, 4, 6, 8, and 10 are all multiples of 2 because $2 \times 1 = 2, 2 \times 2 = 4$, and so on.

multiplication The operation used to find the total number of things in several equal groups or to find the number of times a number repeats.

multiplication/division diagram A diagram used to represent problems in which the total number of objects in several equal groups is being considered. The diagram has three parts: number of groups, number in each group, and total number.

array A group of objects placed in rows and columns.

factor A number that is multiplied.

product The result of multiplication.

In the number model
4 × 3 = 12,
4 and **3** are the **factors,**
and **12** is the **product.**

equal groups Sets with the same number of elements, such as tables with 4 legs, rows with 6 chairs, boxes of 100 paper clips, and so on.

dividend The total before sharing.

divisor The number of equal parts, or the number in each equal part.

quotient The result of division.

In the number model
28 ÷ 4 = 7,
28 is the **dividend,**
4 is the **divisor,** and
7 is the **quotient.**

remainder The amount left over when things are divided into equal shares. In the division number model $16 \div 3 \rightarrow 5$ R1, the remainder is 1.

square number The product of a number multiplied by itself; any number that can be represented by a square array.

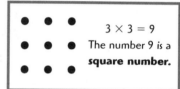

$3 \times 3 = 9$
The number 9 is a
square number.

Building Skills through Games

In Unit 4, your child will practice division and multiplication by playing the following games. For detailed instructions, see the *Student Reference Book.*

Division Arrays

Players make arrays with counters using number cards to determine the number of counters and a toss of a die to establish the number of rows.

Beat the Calculator

A "Calculator" (a player who uses a calculator) and a "Brain" (a player who solves the problem without a calculator) compete to see who will be first to solve multiplication problems.

Use with Lesson 3.9.

Do-Anytime Activities

To work with your child on concepts taught in this unit and in previous units,
try these interesting and rewarding activities:

1 Together with your child, sort objects into equal groups. Discuss what you could do with any
leftover objects.

2 Review multiplication-fact shortcuts:

- **turn-around facts** The order of the factors does not change the product. Thus, if you know
  $3 \times 4 = 12$, you also know $4 \times 3 = 12$.

- **multiplication by 1** The product of 1 and another number is always equal to the other
  number. For example, $1 \times 9 = 9$; $1 \times 7 = 7$.

- **multiplication by 0** The product of 0 and another number is always zero. For example,
  $4 \times 0 = 0$; $0 \times 2 = 0$.

- **square numbers** Arrays for numbers multiplied by themselves are always squares. For example,
  2×2 and 4×4 are square numbers.

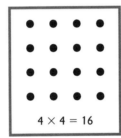

$4 \times 4 = 16$

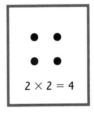

$2 \times 2 = 4$

3 Use the $\times, \div$ Fact Triangles (a set will be sent home later) to practice the basic facts. Act as a
partner by covering one number on the card and then asking your child to create
a multiplication or division number model using the other two numbers.

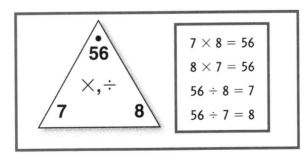

4 Write any number—for example, 34,056. Then ask questions like the following:
How many thousands are there? *(4)* What is the value of the digit 5? *(50)*

5 Ask questions like the following:
Is $467 + 518$ more or less than 1,000? *(less)* Is $754 - 268$ more or less than 500? *(less)*

As You Help Your Child with Homework

As your child brings home assignments, you may want to go over the instructions together, clarifying them as necessary. The answers listed below will guide you through this unit's Home Links.

Home Link 4.1

1. 30 apples   **2.** 60 cupcakes

Home Link 4.2

1. 24 counters   **2.** 24 counters

3. 24 counters

Home Link 4.3

1. 5 counters per person; 0 counters remaining

2. 2 counters per person; 5 counters remaining

3. 4 weeks in January; 3 days remaining

4. 4 teams; 2 children remaining

5. 2 pencils; 4 pencils left over

6. 11 jelly beans; 0 jelly beans left over

7. 8 shelves

Home Link 4.4

1. 6 marbles; 0 marbles left over

2. 2 cookies; 1 cookie left over

3. 4 complete rows; 6 stamps left over

Home Link 4.5

1. 10; 10   **2.** 15; 15   **3.** 20; 20   **4.** 9; 9

5. 90; 90   **6.** 365; 365   **7.** 0; 0   **8.** 0; 0

9. 0; 0   **10.** 20   **11.** 20   **12.** 18

13. 14   **14.** 15   **15.** 50

Home Link 4.6

1. 10; 10; 10; 10   **2.** 12; 12; 12; 12

3. $2 \times 7 = 14$; $7 \times 2 = 14$;
$14 \div 2 = 7$; $14 \div 7 = 2$

4. $2 \times 8 = 16$; $8 \times 2 = 16$;
$16 \div 2 = 8$; $16 \div 8 = 2$

5. $5 \times 4 = 20$; $4 \times 5 = 20$;
$20 \div 5 = 4$; $20 \div 4 = 5$

6. $10 \times 6 = 60$; $6 \times 10 = 60$;
$60 \div 10 = 6$; $60 \div 6 = 10$

Home Link 4.7

1. $5 \times 6 = 30$; $6 \times 5 = 30$; $30 \div 6 = 5$; $30 \div 5 = 6$

2. $8 \times 3 = 24$; $3 \times 8 = 24$; $24 \div 3 = 8$; $24 \div 8 = 3$

3. $2 \times 9 = 18$; $9 \times 2 = 18$; $18 \div 2 = 9$; $18 \div 9 = 2$

4. $4 \times 7 = 28$; $7 \times 4 = 28$; $28 \div 7 = 4$; $28 \div 4 = 7$

5. $9 \times 8 = 72$; $8 \times 9 = 72$; $72 \div 9 = 8$; $72 \div 8 = 9$

6. $6 \times 7 = 42$; $7 \times 6 = 42$; $42 \div 7 = 6$; $42 \div 6 = 7$

Home Link 4.8

1. 5; 7; $7 \times 5 = 35$; 35 square units

2. 7; 6; $6 \times 7 = 42$; 42 square units

3. $4 \times 8 = 32$

4. $5 \times 9 = 45$

Home Link 4.9

The following answers should be circled:

1. more than the distance from Chicago to Dallas; about 2,400 miles

2. about 600 miles;
less than the distance from Chicago to Denver

3. more than the distance from New York to Chicago

4. less than the distance from Denver to Atlanta;
more than the distance from New York to Portland;
about 750 miles

Multiplication Number Stories

Family Note

Today your child learned about another tool to use when solving number stories. We call it a multiplication/division diagram. Diagrams like this can help your child organize the information in a problem. When the information is organized, your child can decide more easily which operation $(+, -, \times, \div)$ will solve the problem. Refer to pages 65, 191, and 192 in the *Student Reference Book* for more information.

Please return this Home Link to school tomorrow.

SRB
65
191 192

For each number story:

• Write the numbers you know. Write ? for the number you need to find.

• Use counters, draw pictures, or do whatever helps you find the answer.

• Write the answer and unit. Check whether your answer makes sense.

1. Meredith buys 5 packages of apples for the party. There are 6 apples in each package. How many apples does she have?

packages	apples per package	total number of apples

Answer: _____
(unit)

2. Max put all of the cupcakes for the bake sale into 10 boxes. He put 6 cupcakes into each box. How many cupcakes was that?

boxes	cupcakes per box	total number of cupcakes

Answer: _____
(unit)

3. Find multiples of equal groups around your home, neighborhood, or nearby store. Record them on the back of this page. *Examples:* 3 lights on each traffic light, 24 soft-drink cans per case

4. Write a multiplication number story about one of your groups. Use the back of this paper. Solve the story.

Arrays

Family Note

Your child is learning how to represent multiplication problems using pictures, called arrays. An array is a group of items arranged in equal rows and equal columns. Help your child use counters, such as pennies or macaroni, to build the array in each problem. Your child should record each solution on the dots next to the problem.

Please return this Home Link to school tomorrow.

For the next few weeks, look for pictures of items arranged in equal rows, or **arrays.** Look in newspapers or magazines. Have people in your family help you. Explain that your class is making an "Arrays Exhibit."

This is a 5-by-6 array.
There are 5 rows.
In each row there are 6 dots. There is a total of 30 dots: $5 \times 6 = 30$.

Make an array with counters. Mark the dots to show the array.

1. 4 rows with 6 counters per row
   a **4-by-6 array**

   _____ counters

2. 3 rows with 8 counters per row
   a **3 × 8 array**

   _____ counters

3. 2 rows with 12 counters per row
   a **2 × 12 array**

   _____ counters

Make up your own.

4. _____ rows with _____ counters per row

   a _____ × _____ **array**

   _____ counters

Division with Counters

Family Note

Your child is beginning to use division while solving number stories. A first step is to use counters to represent each problem. This will help your child understand the meaning of division. Your child will memorize division facts later in the year.

Please return this Home Link to school tomorrow.

Show someone at home how to do division using pennies, macaroni, or other counters.

1. 25 counters are shared equally by 5 people.

_____ counters per person

_____ counters remaining

2. 25 counters are shared equally by 10 people.

_____ counters per person

_____ counters remaining

3. There are 31 days in January.

7 days per week

_____ weeks in January

_____ days remaining

4. There are 22 children.

5 children per team

_____ teams

_____ children remaining

---

5. Mrs. March has 34 pencils to give to the 15 students in her music class.

How many pencils can she give each student? _____ pencils

How many pencils are left over? _____ pencils

6. Caleb shared 22 jelly beans with his sister. How many jelly beans did each child get?

_____ jelly beans _____ jelly beans left over

7. Marta has 30 books to put on shelves. Each shelf holds 4 books.

How many shelves will she need? _____ shelves

Division Number Stories

Family Note

If your child is having difficulty solving the division number stories, help him or her by using counters to find the solutions. For example, you might use a set of small objects, such as pennies, uncooked pasta, or pebbles, to model the problems. Refer to pages 67, 68, 191, and 192 in the *Student Reference Book.* Your child is not expected to know division facts at this time.

Please return this Home Link to school tomorrow.

SRB
67 68
191 192

Show someone at home how you can use division to solve these number stories. Fill in the diagrams.

1. Carlos gave 24 marbles to 4 friends. Each friend got the same number of marbles. How many marbles did each friend get?

friends	marbles per friend	total number of marbles

_____ marbles

How many marbles were left over? _____ marbles

2. Allie had 29 cookies to put in 14 lunch bags. She put the same number in each bag. How many cookies did she put in each bag?

bags	cookies per bag	total number of cookies

_____ cookies

How many cookies were left over? _____ cookie(s)

3. A sheet of stamps has 46 stamps. A complete row has 10 stamps. How many complete rows are there?

complete rows	stamps per row	total number of stamps

_____ complete rows

How many stamps are left over? _____ stamps

Multiplication-Fact Shortcuts

Family Note

Your child is learning the basic multiplication facts. Listen to your child explain multiplication-fact shortcuts as he or she works the problems. Review some 1s, 2s, 5s, and 10s multiplication facts (facts like $1 \times 3 = ?$, $? = 2 \times 4$, $5 \times 5 = ?$, and $10 \times 4 = ?$).

Please return this Home Link to school tomorrow.

Tell someone at home about multiplication-fact shortcuts.

The turn-around rule: $3 \times 4 = 12$ helps me know $4 \times 3 = 12$.

1. $2 \times 5 =$ _____ and $5 \times 2 =$ _____

2. _____ $= 5 \times 3$ and _____ $= 3 \times 5$

3. $10 \times 2 =$ _____ and $2 \times 10 =$ _____

If 1 is multiplied by any number, the product is that number.
The same is true if any number is multiplied by 1.

4. _____ $= 1 \times 9$ and _____ $= 9 \times 1$

5. $1 \times 90 =$ _____ and $90 \times 1 =$ _____

6. $365 \times 1 =$ _____ and $1 \times 365 =$ _____

If 0 is multiplied by any number, the product is 0.
The same is true if any number is multiplied by 0.

7. $0 \times 12 =$ _____ and $12 \times 0 =$ _____

8. $99 \times 0 =$ _____ and $0 \times 99 =$ _____

9. _____ $= 9{,}365 \times 0$ and _____ $= 0 \times 9{,}365$

Think about counting by 2s, 5s, and 10s.

10.	**11.**	**12.**	**13.**	**14.**	**15.**
10	5	9	2	5	10
$\times 2$	$\times 4$	$\times 2$	$\times 7$	$\times 3$	$\times 5$

×, ÷ Fact Triangles

Family Note

Fact Triangles are tools for building mental-math reflexes. You might think of them as the *Everyday Mathematics* version of the flash cards that you remember from grade school. Fact Triangles are more effective for helping children memorize facts, however, because they emphasize fact families.

A **fact family** is a collection of related facts made from the same 3 numbers. For the numbers 4, 6, and 24, for example, the multiplication/division fact family consists of 4 × 6 = 24, 6 × 4 = 24, 24 ÷ 6 = 4, and 24 ÷ 4 = 6.

You can use Fact Triangles to practice multiplication facts with your child.

Cut out the Fact Triangles from the two sheets attached to this letter.

Then, to practice multiplication with your child, first cover the number by the large dot—the product—with your thumb.

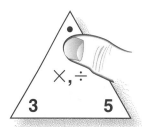

Your child should tell you one or two multiplication facts: 3 × 5 = 15 or 5 × 3 = 15.

To practice division, cover one of the smaller numbers with your thumb.

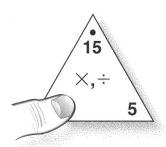

Your child should now tell you the division fact 15 ÷ 5 = 3.

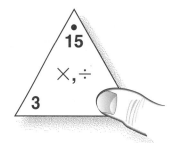

Your child should now tell you the division fact 15 ÷ 3 = 5.

If your child misses a fact, flash the other two fact problems on the card and then return to the fact that was missed. *Example:* Sue can't answer 15 ÷ 3. Flash 3 × 5, and then 15 ÷ 5, and finally 15 ÷ 3 a second time.

Make this activity brief and fun. Spend about 10 minutes each night for the next few weeks or until your child masters all of the facts. The work you do at home will support the work we are doing at school.

*Please return the **second page** of this Home Link to school tomorrow.*

SRB
48   49

Name _____ Date _____ Time _____

✕,÷ Fact Triangles (cont.)

Home Link
4.6

Tell someone at home about multiplication/division fact families.

1. The numbers 2, 5, and 10 form the following facts:

2 × 5 = _____   _____ ÷ 2 = 5

5 × 2 = _____   _____ ÷ 5 = 2

2. Knowing 6 × 2 = _____ and 2 × 6 = _____

helps me know _____ ÷ 2 = 6 and _____ ÷ 6 = 2.

3. The numbers 2, 7, and 14 form this multiplication/division fact family:

_____   _____

_____   _____

Write the fact family for each multiplication/division Fact Triangle.

4.
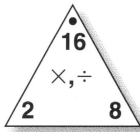

5.
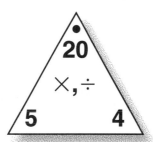

6.

/60\
×,÷
10   6

_____   _____   _____

_____   _____   _____

_____   _____   _____

_____   _____   _____

Use with Lesson 4.6.

89

Fact Families

Family Note

Your child continues to practice multiplication in school. You can help by stressing the relationship between multiplication and division: With the three nonzero numbers in a multiplication fact, two division facts can be formed. Fact Triangles are designed to help children understand this concept.

Please return this Home Link to school tomorrow.

Write the fact family for each Fact Triangle.

1.

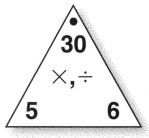

30
×,÷
5   6

_____ × _____ = _____

_____ × _____ = _____

_____ ÷ _____ = _____

_____ ÷ _____ = _____

2.

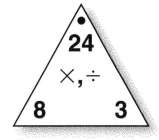

24
×,÷
8   3

_____ × _____ = _____

_____ × _____ = _____

_____ ÷ _____ = _____

_____ ÷ _____ = _____

3.

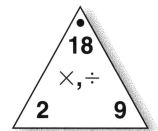

18
×,÷
2   9

_____ × _____ = _____

_____ × _____ = _____

_____ ÷ _____ = _____

_____ ÷ _____ = _____

4.

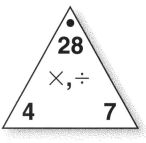

28
×,÷
4   7

_____ × _____ = _____

_____ × _____ = _____

_____ ÷ _____ = _____

_____ ÷ _____ = _____

5.

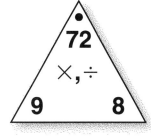

72
×,÷
9   8

_____ × _____ = _____

_____ × _____ = _____

_____ ÷ _____ = _____

_____ ÷ _____ = _____

6.

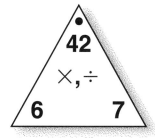

42
×,÷
6   7

_____ × _____ = _____

_____ × _____ = _____

_____ ÷ _____ = _____

_____ ÷ _____ = _____

Arrays and Areas

Family Note

Your child uses the same procedure for finding the area of a rectangle that is used for finding the number of dots in an array. For Problem 3 it does not matter whether your child draws an array with 4 rows of 8 dots or 8 rows of 4 dots. What is important is that the array has two sides that have 4 dots and two sides that have 8 dots. The same is true for Problem 4.

Please return this Home Link to school tomorrow.

Make a dot inside each small square in one row. Then fill in the blanks.

1. Number of squares in a row: _____

Number of rows: _____

Number model: _____ × _____ = _____

Area: _____ square units

2. Number of squares in a row: _____

Number of rows: _____

Number model: _____ × _____ = _____

Area: _____ square units

Mark the dots to show each array. Then fill in the blanks.

3. Make a 4-by-8 array.

Number model: _____ × _____ = _____

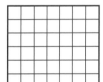

4. Make a 5-by-9 array.

Number model: _____ × _____ = _____

Using a Map Scale

Family Note

Your child is just learning how to use a map scale. The distances given on the map are "as the crow flies." This means that the distances are for the most direct route from point to point. Such estimates give useful information about the relative distances between locations. Actual road distances are longer than these direct paths.

Please return this Home Link to school tomorrow.

For each question, circle all reasonable answers. (There may be more than one reasonable answer.) All distances are "as the crow flies." Be sure to use the map scale on the next page.

1. About how many miles is it from New York to Los Angeles?

about 1,000 miles

more than the distance from Chicago to Dallas

about 2,400 miles

2. About how many miles is it from Chicago to Atlanta?

about 600 miles

more than the distance from Chicago to Seattle

less than the distance from Chicago to Denver

3. About how many miles is it from Seattle to Dallas?

about 2,600 miles

about 5,000 miles

more than the distance from New York to Chicago

4. About how many miles is it from New York to Atlanta?

less than the distance from Denver to Atlanta

more than the distance from New York to Portland

about 750 miles

Using a Map Scale (cont.)

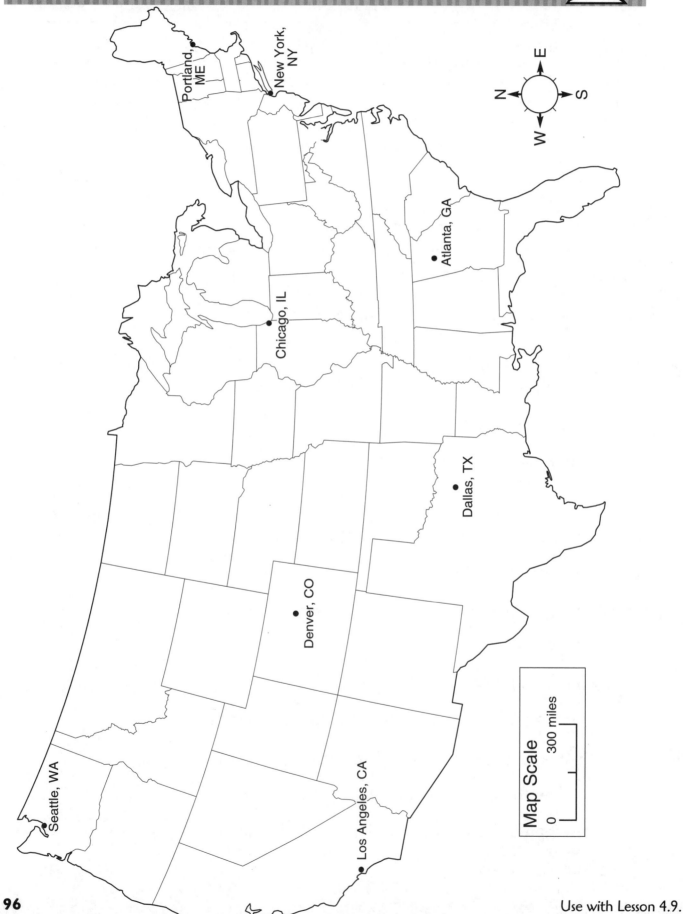

Use with Lesson 4.9.

Family Letter

Unit 5: Place Value in Whole Numbers and Decimals

In Unit 5, children will review place value in whole numbers through ten-thousands and then explore place value to the millions. They will practice reading, writing, and ordering 4- and 5-digit numbers before moving on to larger numbers.

To understand real-life applications of large numbers, children will study population data about U.S. cities. They will also work with large numbers as they approximate their own ages to the minute.

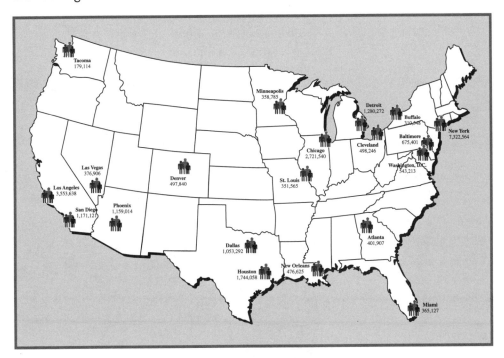

In second grade, children studied decimals to the hundredths place by working with money. In this unit, they will gradually extend their knowledge of decimals through thousandths. First, children will use concrete models, such as base-10 blocks. Then they will write decimal values using three different kinds of notation. For example, 0.1, one-tenth, and $\frac{1}{10}$ are all names for the same number.

Later in this unit, children will compare and order numbers using the less-than ($<$), greater-than ($>$), and equal ($=$) symbols.

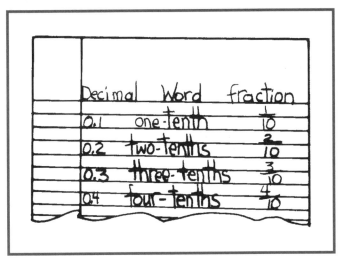

Decimal	Word	Fraction
0.1	one-tenth	$\frac{1}{10}$
0.2	two-tenths	$\frac{2}{10}$
0.3	three-tenths	$\frac{3}{10}$
0.4	four-tenths	$\frac{4}{10}$

Please keep this Family Letter for reference as your child works through Unit 5.

Vocabulary

Important terms in Unit 5:

The *value* of each digit in a numeral is determined by its *place* in the numeral. Use the following chart to identify the **thousands, hundreds, tens, ones, tenths, hundredths,** and **thousandths** values in the numeral 4,815.904 (read as "four thousand, eight hundred fifteen, and nine hundred four thousandths"):

thousands	hundreds	tens	ones		tenths	hundredths	thousandths
4	8	1	5	.	9	0	4
Each thousand is equal to one thousand times the unit value.	Each hundred is equal to one hundred times the unit value.	Each ten is equal to ten times the unit value.	Each one is equal to the unit value.		Each tenth is equal to $\frac{1}{10}$ of the unit value.	Each hundredth is equal to $\frac{1}{100}$ of the unit value.	Each thousandth is equal to $\frac{1}{1,000}$ of the unit value.
(4,000)	(800)	(10)	(5)		$\left(\frac{9}{10}\right)$	$\left(\frac{0}{100}\right)$	$\left(\frac{4}{1,000}\right)$

maximum The largest amount, or the greatest number in a set of data.

millimeter In the metric system, a unit of length equivalent to $\frac{1}{10}$ of a centimeter and $\frac{1}{1,000}$ of a meter.

pie graph A graph in which a circle is divided into parts to represent the parts of a set of data. The circle represents the whole set of data.

line graph A drawing that shows the relationships among data by using a set of points connected by line segments; often used to show trends.

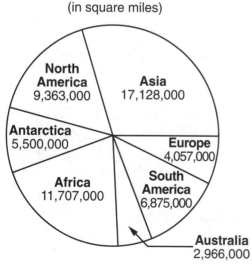

Areas of the Continents
(in square miles)

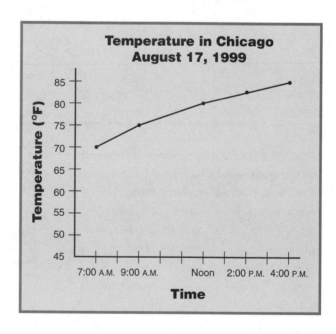

Use with Lesson 4.10.

Do-Anytime Activities

To work with your child on the concepts taught in this unit and in previous units,
try these interesting and rewarding activities:

1 Dictate large numbers for your child to write. *Examples:* 4,123; 10,032; 2,368,502.

2 Display similar multidigit numbers on a calculator for your child to read.

3 Together, write 5 multidigit numbers in order from smallest to largest.

4 Start at any whole number and, using a calculator, count on by increments of 0.01 or 0.1.

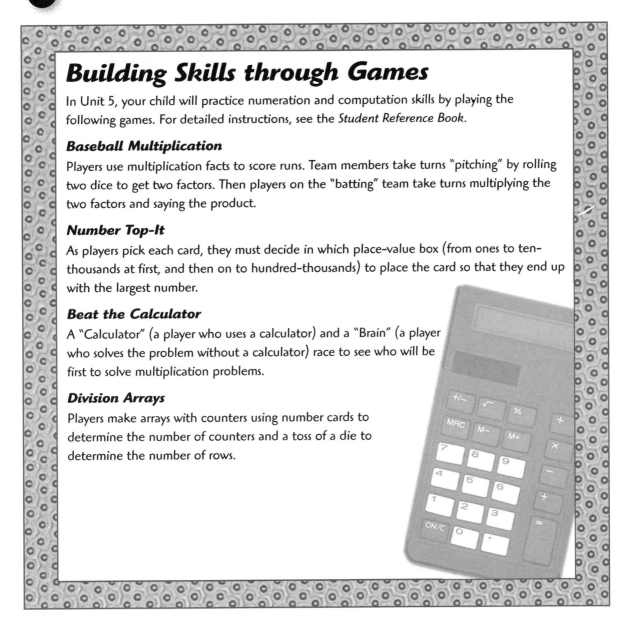

Building Skills through Games

In Unit 5, your child will practice numeration and computation skills by playing the
following games. For detailed instructions, see the *Student Reference Book.*

Baseball Multiplication

Players use multiplication facts to score runs. Team members take turns "pitching" by rolling
two dice to get two factors. Then players on the "batting" team take turns multiplying the
two factors and saying the product.

Number Top-It

As players pick each card, they must decide in which place-value box (from ones to ten-
thousands at first, and then on to hundred-thousands) to place the card so that they end up
with the largest number.

Beat the Calculator

A "Calculator" (a player who uses a calculator) and a "Brain" (a player
who solves the problem without a calculator) race to see who will be
first to solve multiplication problems.

Division Arrays

Players make arrays with counters using number cards to
determine the number of counters and a toss of a die to
determine the number of rows.

As You Help Your Child with Homework

As your child brings home assignments, you may want to go over the instructions together, clarifying them as necessary. The answers listed below will guide you through this unit's Home Links.

Home Link 5.1

1. 7,889; 8,889; 9,889; 10,889; 11,889; 12,889

2. 8,789; 8,889; 8,989; 9,089; 9,189; 9,289

3. 8,879; 8,889; 8,899; 8,909; 8,919; 8,929

Home Link 5.2

1. < **2.** > **3.** <

4. < **5.** > **6.** <

7. 3,689 **8.** 9,863 **10.** 4 thousands, or 4,000

11. 5 ten-thousands, or 50,000

12. 0 tens, or 0

13. 50,100; 51,100; 52,100; 53,100

Home Link 5.3

1. largest: 7,654,321
smallest: 1,234,567
total: 8,888,888

3. 7,037,562
7,000,007
4,056,211
104,719
42,876
25,086
9,603
784

4. 42,876

5. 7,037,562

6. 4,056,211

7. 7,000,007

Home Link 5.4

1. 7 continents **2.** Asia **3.** Australia

4. Antarctica, North America, and South America

5. Europe

6. North America

7. Africa

Home Link 5.7

1. $\frac{3}{10}$ or $\frac{30}{100}$; 0.3 or 0.30 **2.** $\frac{9}{100}$; 0.09

3. $\frac{65}{100}$; 0.65 **4.** 0.3; 0.65; 0.65

5. **6.** **7.**

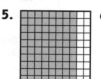

8. 0.04, 0.53, 0.8

Home Link 5.8

1. 57 hundredths; 5 tenths 7 hundredths

2. 70 hundredths; 7 tenths 0 hundredths

3. 4 hundredths; 0 tenths 4 hundredths

4. 0.23 **5.** 8.4 **6.** 30.20 **7.** 0.05

8. 0.4, 0.5, 0.6 **9.** 0.04, 0.05, 0.06

10. 1.00, 1.10, 1.20 **11.** 0.10, 0.11, 0.12

12. twelve-hundredths **13.** six and one-tenth

Home Link 5.9

4. 0.6 **5.** 0.4 **6.** 0.17

7. 0.53 **8.** 0.2 **9.** 0.99

10.–13.

D A   B   C

0 1 2 3 4 5 6 7 8 9 10 11 12 13 14 15
cm

Home Link 5.10

2. a. 2 **b.** 10 **c.** 20 **d.** 100 **e.** 200 **f.** 600

3. a. 30 centimeters **b.** 0.3 meter **c.** 300 millimeters

Home Link 5.11

1. < **2.** < **3.** > **4.** =

5. > **6.** < **7.** = **8.** <

9. 9 hundredths, or 0.09 **10.** 3 ones, or 3

11. 8 thousandths, or 0.008 **12.** 6.59, 6.60, 6.61

13. 1.03, 1.13, 1.23 **14.** 3.009, 3.010, 3.011

15. 4.4 **16.** 4.17 **17.** 9.0 **18.** 6.03

19. 8.1 **20.** 5.53 **21.** 2.9 **22.** 7.2

Frames and Arrows

Family Note

Have your child read and solve the three Frames-and-Arrows problems. Review the rule that is being used in each puzzle. Ask your child to look for patterns in the frames. For example, which digit changes when adding or subtracting 1,000? *(thousands digit)* 100? *(hundreds digit and thousands digit when moving from the 8,000s to the 9,000s)* 10? *(tens digit and hundreds digit when moving from the 8,800s to the 8,900s)*

Please return this Home Link to school tomorrow.

Solve each Frames-and-Arrows problem.

1.

Rule
Add 1,000

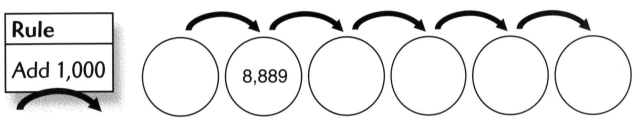

2.

Rule
Add 100

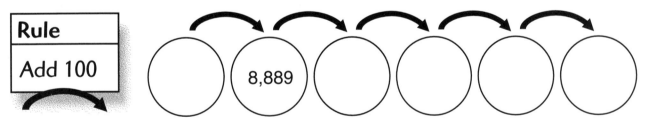

3.

Rule
Add 10

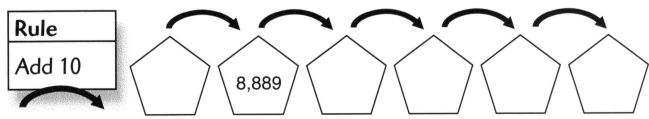

Comparing Numbers

Family Note

Review the meanings of the > and < relation symbols before your child begins this page. *Number Top-It* (5-Digit Numbers) on *Student Reference Book* pages 226 and 227 allows children to practice comparing 5-digit numbers. You may wish to play this game with your child. When your child has completed the Home Link, ask him or her to read the numbers on the page to you.

Please return this Home Link to school tomorrow.

SRB
226 227

Write < or >.

1. 906 ____ 960

2. 5,708 ____ 599

3. 31,859 ____ 31,958

4. 10,006 ____ 10,106

5. 48,936 ____ 4,971

6. 76,094 ____ 76,111

> < means "is
> less than"
> > means "is
> greater than"

Use the digits 6, 8, 3, and 9.

7. Write the smallest number possible. _____

8. Write the largest number possible. _____

9. Write two numbers between the smallest and largest numbers.

_____   _____

The 7 in 7,462 stands for 7 __*thousands*__ or __*7,000*__.

10. The 4 in 64,308 stands for 4 _____ or _____.

11. The 5 in 53,789 stands for 5 _____ or _____.

12. The 0 in 76,809 stands for 0 _____ or _____.

Fill in the missing numbers.

13.

50,100 _____ _____ 53,100

Practice with Place Value

Family Note

Help your child use the seven digit squares to make the largest and smallest whole numbers possible out of all seven digits. *Number Top-It* (7-Digit Numbers) on *Student Reference Book* page 228 provides practice comparing 7-digit numbers. You may wish to play this game with your child.

Please return this Home Link to school tomorrow.

SRB
228

---

1. Cut out the digit squares. Use all 7 digits to make the largest number and the smallest. Add the numbers and then read them to someone at home.

largest _____

smallest _____

Total _____

2. Read the following numbers to someone at home:

784   25,086   4,056,211   42,876

9,603   7,000,007   7,037,562   104,719

3. Write the numbers above in order from the largest to the smallest.

_____
(largest)

_____

_____

_____

_____

_____

_____
(smallest)

4. Which number is 1,000 less than 43,876?

_____

5. Which number is 10,000 more than 7,027,562?

_____

6. Which number is 10,000 less than 4,066,211?

_____

7. Which number is 1,000,000 more than 6,000,007?

_____

| 6 |
| 2 |
| 4 |
| 7 |
| 1 |
| 5 |
| 3 |

Comparing Areas of Continents

Family Note

Your child has been practicing reading and writing 6- and 7-digit numerals. Use the pie graph to help him or her answer the questions about the continents. Ask your child to read each of the areas aloud to you. Encourage rounding the areas to the nearest million when making the comparisons in Problems 5–7. Remember that working with numbers in the millions is a new skill for your child.

Please return this Home Link to school tomorrow.

Use the graph to answer the questions.

Areas of the Continents
(in square miles)

1. How many continents are there?

   _____

2. Which continent has the largest area?

   _____

3. Which continent has the smallest area?

   _____

4. Which continents have an area between 5 and 10 million square miles each?

   _____

   _____

North America 9,363,000

Asia 17,128,000

Antarctica 5,500,000

Europe 4,057,000

Africa 11,707,000

South America 6,875,000

Australia 2,966,000

5. Which continent is about 1 million square miles larger than Australia? _____

6. Which continent is a little more than half the size of Asia? _____

Challenge

7. Which continent is a little less than 3 times the size of Europe?

   _____

Writing and Ordering Numbers

Family Note

Observe and encourage as your child makes 4-digit numbers using the digit squares and then records the numbers and writes them in order, from smallest to largest. Then listen as your child reads the numbers to you.

Please return this Home Link to school tomorrow.

Cut out the digit squares. Arrange them into 4-digit numbers in as many different ways as you can. Record each number you make. Then put the numbers in order from smallest to largest. Read your numbers to someone at home.

Record numbers here: **Order** numbers here:

_____

_____ (smallest)

_____   _____

_____   _____

_____   _____

_____   _____

_____   _____   **3**

_____   _____

_____   _____   **5**

_____   _____

_____   _____   **8**

_____   _____

_____   _____   **3**

_____   _____

_____   _____ (largest)

Stories with Large Numbers

Family Note

Help your child write an addition and a subtraction story. Include large numbers in both stories. Your child has been working with numbers as large as millions (7 digits), so this is a realistic expectation. However, it is perfectly acceptable for children to make up stories with 5- or 6-digit numbers.

Please return this Home Link to school tomorrow.

For each number story, try to think about large numbers of things. Share your stories with someone at home. If the numbers are too big for you to add or subtract, use a calculator or ask someone at home to help.

1. Write a number story that you solve by adding.   **Workspace**

_____

_____

_____

_____

Answer: _____
                    (unit)

2. Write a number story that you solve by subtracting.

_____

_____

_____

_____

Answer: _____
                    (unit)

Understanding Decimals

Family Note

Your child has been using grids like the ones below to understand the meaning of decimals. The grid is made up of 100 squares. Each square is $\frac{1}{100}$ or 0.01 of the grid. Ten squares is $\frac{1}{10}$ or 0.10 of the grid. 0.8 is read as "eight-tenths." 0.04 is read as "four-hundredths." 0.53 is read as "fifty-three hundredths."

Please return this Home Link to school tomorrow.

If the grid is ONE, then what part of each grid is shaded?
Write a decimal and a fraction below each grid.

1.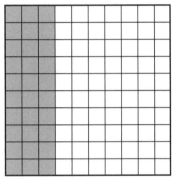

fraction: _____

decimal: _____

2.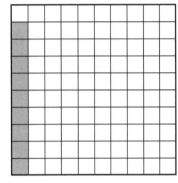

fraction: _____

decimal: _____

3.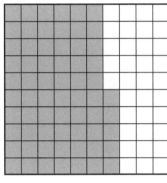

fraction: _____

decimal: _____

4. Which decimal is greater? Use the grids to help you.

0.3 or 0.09 _____   0.09 or 0.65 _____   0.3 or 0.65 _____

5. Color 0.8 of the grid.

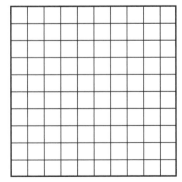

6. Color 0.04 of the grid.

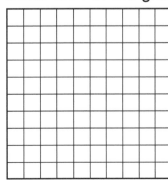

7. Color 0.53 of the grid.

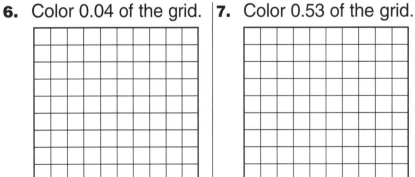

8. Write 0.8, 0.04, and 0.53 in order from smallest to largest.
Use the grids to help you. _____ _____ _____

Name _____   Date _____   Time _____

Tenths and Hundredths

Home Link 5.8

Family Note

Your child continues to work with decimals, now with tenths and hundredths. If your child has difficulty continuing the counts in Problems 8–11, encourage him or her to think in terms of dollars-and-cents notation for money. For example, $0.07 (7 cents), $0.08 (8 cents), $0.09 (9 cents), $0.10 (10 cents), and so on.

Please return this Home Link to school tomorrow.

Write what each diagram shows.

1.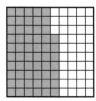

_____ hundredths

___ tenths ___ hundredths

2.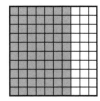

_____ hundredths

___ tenths ___ hundredths

3.

_____ hundredths

___ tenths ___ hundredths

Write the words as decimal numbers.

4. twenty-three hundredths

_____

5. eight and four-tenths

_____

6. thirty and twenty-hundredths

_____

7. five-hundredths

_____

Continue each pattern.

8. 0.1, 0.2, 0.3, _____, _____, _____

9. 0.01, 0.02, 0.03, _____, _____, _____

10. 0.70, 0.80, 0.90, _____, _____, _____

11. 0.07, 0.08, 0.09, _____, _____, _____

Write each decimal in words.

12. 0.12 _____

13. 6.1 _____

Use with Lesson 5.8.

115

Name   Date   Time

Practice with Decimals   Home Link
                                                          5.9

Family Note

Your child has been practicing decimal notation for use in metric measurement and practicing converting from centimeters to meters. The following equivalencies will assist you in helping your child solve Problems 10–13: 1 cm =10 mm, 1 m = 100 cm, 1 m = 1,000 mm.

Please return this Home Link to school tomorrow.

Fill in the missing numbers.

1.

0   0.01   ____   ____   ____   ____   ____   0.08

2.

0.05   0.06   ____   ____   ____   ____   0.12   ____

3.

0.7   ____   ____   ____   ____   ____   ____   1.5

Circle the decimal that is greater.

4. 0.6 or 0.14   **5.** 0.07 or 0.4   **6.** 0.17 or 0.03

7. 0.53 or 0.35   **8.** 0.05 or 0.2   **9.** 0.4 or 0.99

Follow these directions on the ruler below.

10. Make a dot at 7 cm and label it with the letter *A*.

11. Make a dot at 90 mm and label it with the letter *B*.

12. Make a dot at 0.13 m and label it with the letter *C*.

13. Make a dot at 0.06 m and label it with the letter *D*.

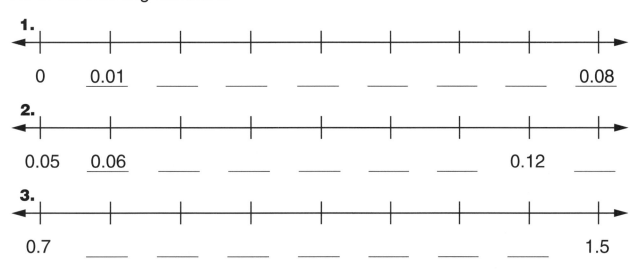

Use with Lesson 5.9.   **117**

Measuring with Millimeters

Family Note

Your child has been using millimeters to learn about decimal place value. This page offers a way to practice with millimeters and other metric measurements. Have your child draw the termite and use the ruler to answer the questions on the page.

Please return this Home Link to school tomorrow.

Pretend that you have a jar full of large queen termites. Each termite is 5 millimeters long. You decide to make a termite chain by placing the termites head-to-tail on a meterstick.

A queen termite shown larger than actual size

1. Draw a termite on the ruler at the bottom of the page.

2. How many termites would fit on

    a. 1 centimeter? _____   **b.** 5 centimeters? _____

    c. 10 centimeters? _____   **d.** 50 centimeters? _____

    e. the whole meterstick? _____   **f.** 3 metersticks? _____

3. What would be the length of a chain of 60 termites?

    a. _____ centimeters **b.** _____ meter **c.** _____ millimeters

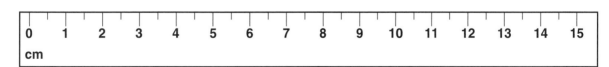

Comparing Decimals

Family Note

Ask your child to read the decimal numerals aloud. If he or she is having difficulty, encourage using the following method:
1. Read the whole-number part.
2. Say "and" for the decimal point.
3. Read the digits after the decimal point as though they formed their own number.
4. Say "tenths," "hundredths," or "thousandths" as appropriate. Encourage your child to exaggerate the "ths" sound.

Please return this Home Link to school tomorrow.

Write <, >, or =.

> means "is greater than"
< means "is less than"

1. 2.35 _____ 2.57   **2.** 1.008 _____ 1.8

3. 0.64 _____ 0.46   **4.** 0.90 _____ 0.9   **5.** 42.1 _____ 42.09

6. 7.098 _____ 7.542   **7.** 0.4 _____ 0.400   **8.** 0.206 _____ 0.214

Example: The 4 in 0.47 stands for 4 <u>tenths</u> or <u>0.4</u>.

9. The 9 in 4.59 stands for 9 _____ or _____.

10. The 3 in 3.62 stands for 3 _____ or _____.

11. The 8 in 5.028 stands for 8 _____ or _____.

Continue each number pattern.

12. 6.56, 6.57, 6.58, _____, _____, _____

13. 0.73, 0.83, 0.93, _____, _____, _____

14. 3.006, 3.007, 3.008, _____, _____, _____

Write the number that is 0.1 more.

15. 4.3 _____   **16.** 4.07 _____   **17.** 8.9 _____   **18.** 5.93 _____

Write the number that is 0.1 less.

19. 8.2 _____   **20.** 5.63 _____   **21.** 3 _____   **22.** 7.1 _____

Graphing Data

Family Note

Your child has learned how to make and read a line graph using length-of-day information that he or she has been collecting throughout the year. This is a new skill, so your child may need help graphing the data on the grid. Help your child see that the baby grows very quickly at first, but then he grows more slowly. Remind your child that adults stay about the same size for the remainder of their lives.

Please return this Home Link to school tomorrow.

1. The table below shows how baby Michael's weight increased until his first birthday. Draw dots to graph the weight of the baby on the grid. Use a straightedge to connect each pair of consecutive dots.

Age (months)	Weight (pounds)
0	8
1	10
2	12
4	15
6	17
9	20
12	22

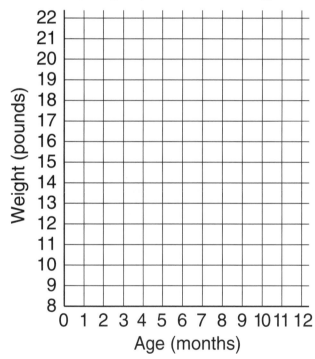

Baby Michael's Weight

2. Why does the line graph keep going up?

_____

3. Do you think the line graph will keep going up forever? Explain.

_____

_____

Unit 6: Geometry

Everyday Mathematics uses children's experiences with the everyday world to help them envision 3-dimensional (3-D) shapes. In previous grades, children were asked to identify 2-dimensional (2-D) shapes and their parts, such as edges and corners (vertices). They had several hands-on experiences with pattern blocks, geoboards, and templates. They also classified and named polygons, or closed figures consisting of line segments (sides) connected endpoint to endpoint.

In Unit 6, children will explore points, line segments, rays, and lines and the relationships among them, along with the geometric shapes that can be built from them. Children will construct angles, polygons, prisms, and pyramids.

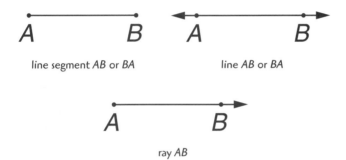

line segment *AB* or *BA*   line *AB* or *BA*

ray *AB*

Children will also explore similarities and differences among 3-D shapes and regular polyhedrons within the context of a Shapes Museum. They will discover real-life examples of lines that are parallel, or lines that never meet, such as railroad tracks.

There is a great deal of specialized vocabulary involved when working with geometry. However, the emphasis in this unit is not on memorizing the vocabulary but rather on using it to examine relationships among and classifications of geometric figures.

Please keep this Family Letter for reference as your child works through Unit 6.

Vocabulary

Important terms in Unit 6:

2-dimensional (2-D) shape A shape that lies completely within a plane, or flat surface.

3-dimensional (3-D) shape An object that does not lie completely within a single flat surface; an object with thickness, as well as length and width.

base A flat surface (face) whose shape is the basis for classifying some 3-dimensional objects.

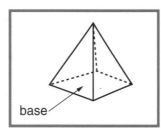

cone A 3-dimensional shape having a circular base, a curved surface, and one vertex. An ice cream cone is a common object shaped like a cone.

sphere
A 3-dimensional shape whose curved surface is, at all points, a given distance from its center point. A ball is shaped like a sphere.

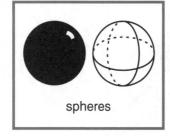

cylinder A 3-dimensional shape having a curved surface and parallel circular bases that are the same size. A can is a common object shaped like a cylinder.

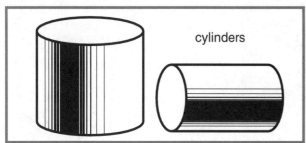

parallel Never meeting; everywhere the same distance apart.

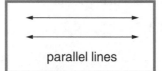

face A flat surface on a 3-dimensional shape.

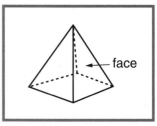

polyhedron
A 3-dimensional shape, all of whose surfaces (faces) are flat, as opposed to curved. Each face is a polygon. Below are five regular polyhedrons.

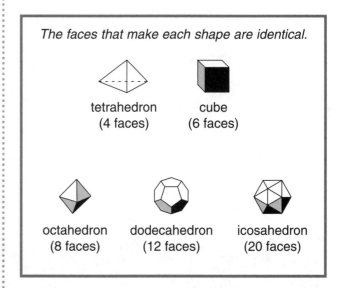

The faces that make each shape are identical.

tetrahedron (4 faces)   cube (6 faces)

octahedron (8 faces)   dodecahedron (12 faces)   icosahedron (20 faces)

prism A polyhedron with two parallel flat surfaces (bases) that are the same size and shape. Prisms are classified according to the shape of the two parallel bases; the sides (faces) are parallelograms.

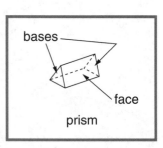

pyramid A polyhedron in which one face (the base) is a polygon and the other faces are triangles with a common vertex. Pyramids are classified according to the shapes of their bases.

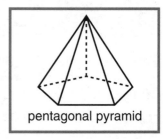

pentagonal pyramid

Use with Lesson 5.13.

Do-Anytime Activities

To work with your child on the concepts taught in this unit and in previous units, try these interesting and rewarding activities:

1 Together, read the book *The Greedy Triangle* by Marilyn Burns.

2 Begin a Shapes Museum at home. Label the shapes that your child collects.

3 Ask your child to identify 2-dimensional and 3-dimensional shapes around the house.

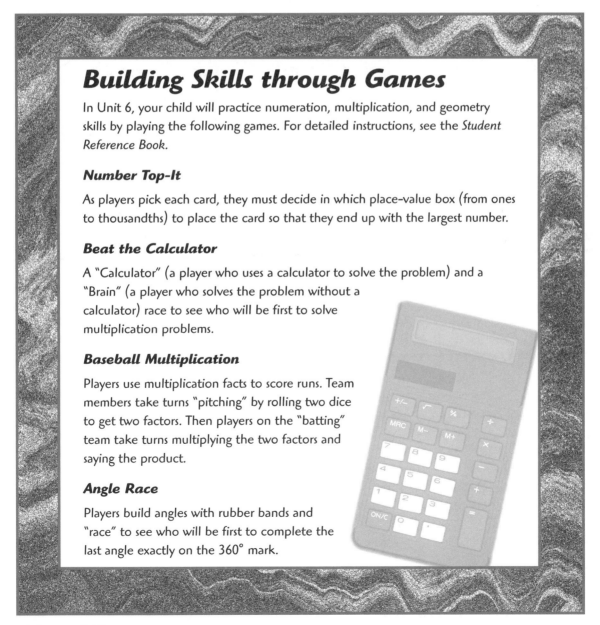

Building Skills through Games

In Unit 6, your child will practice numeration, multiplication, and geometry skills by playing the following games. For detailed instructions, see the *Student Reference Book*.

Number Top-It

As players pick each card, they must decide in which place-value box (from ones to thousandths) to place the card so that they end up with the largest number.

Beat the Calculator

A "Calculator" (a player who uses a calculator to solve the problem) and a "Brain" (a player who solves the problem without a calculator) race to see who will be first to solve multiplication problems.

Baseball Multiplication

Players use multiplication facts to score runs. Team members take turns "pitching" by rolling two dice to get two factors. Then players on the "batting" team take turns multiplying the two factors and saying the product.

Angle Race

Players build angles with rubber bands and "race" to see who will be first to complete the last angle exactly on the 360° mark.

As You Help Your Child with Homework

As your child brings home assignments, you may want to go over the instructions together, clarifying them as necessary. The answers listed below will guide you through this unit's Home Links.

Home Link 6.1

2.

3.

4.

5. Sample answer:

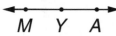

Home Link 6.2

Sample answers:

1.

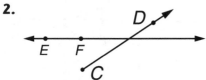

2.

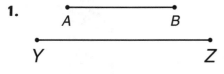

3.

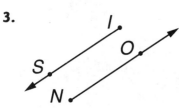

4.

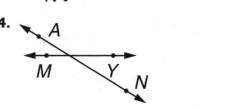

5.   **6.**

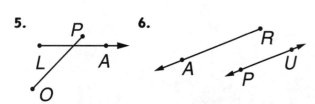

Home Link 6.5

1. equal; right angles; parallel

2. right angles; equal; parallel

3. equal; parallel

4. equal; parallel

5. equal

Home Link 6.6

Sample answers:

1. 4; kite; *XENA*   **2.** 6; hexagon; *JORDAN*

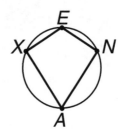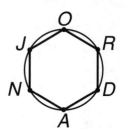

Home Link 6.8

1. *A*   **2.** *D*   **3.** *E*

4. *C* or *D*   **5.** *B*

Home Link 6.9

1. a. triangle   **b.** 2 sides   **c.** 2 angles   **d.** no

2. a. square   **b.** yes

Home Link 6.11

1. (from left to right) prism; sphere; cylinder; cone; pyramid

Home Link 6.12

1. pentagonal prism   **2.** pentagon

3. rectangle   **4.** 15 edges

5. 10 vertices

   Use with Lesson 5.13.

Line Segments, Rays, and Lines

 Family Note

Help your child match each name below with the correct drawing of a line, ray, or line segment. Then observe as your child uses a straightedge to draw more named figures. Pages 88 and 89 in the *Student Reference Book* discuss these figures.

Please return this Home Link to school tomorrow.

 SRB 88 89

This line segment can be named $\overline{AB}$ or $\overline{BA}$.

A   B

Each of these rays can be named $\overrightarrow{YZ}$.

Y   Z   Z   Y

This line can be named $\overleftrightarrow{AB}$, $\overleftrightarrow{BA}$, $\overleftrightarrow{AC}$, $\overleftrightarrow{CA}$, $\overleftrightarrow{BC}$, or $\overleftrightarrow{CB}$.

A   B   C

1. Match each drawing below with one of the names.

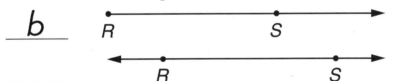
___b___ R   S

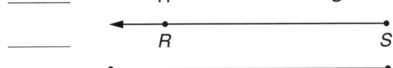
_____ R   S

_____ R   S

_____ S   T

_____ R   S   T

a. $\overline{TS}$

b. $\overrightarrow{RS}$

c. $\overleftrightarrow{TS}$

d. $\overrightarrow{SR}$

e. $\overleftrightarrow{RS}$

Follow the directions carefully. Use a straightedge.

2. Mark points *B* and *C*. Draw a line segment, $\overline{BC}$.

3. Draw a ray, $\overrightarrow{TO}$.

4. Draw a line, $\overleftrightarrow{AT}$.

5. Draw a line, $\overleftrightarrow{MY}$. Mark a point, *A*, on the line.

More Line Segments, Rays, and Lines

Family Note

Refer to the following notations to help your child draw and label line segments, rays, and lines.

line segment *AB*	$\overline{AB}$	
ray *BA*	$\overrightarrow{BA}$	
line *AB*	$\overleftrightarrow{AB}$	

Please return this Home Link to school tomorrow.

Use a straightedge and a sharp pencil to draw the following. Be sure to mark points and label the line segments, rays, and lines.

1. Draw a line segment, $\overline{YZ}$, that is parallel to $\overline{AB}$.

2. Draw a ray, $\overrightarrow{CD}$, that intersects $\overleftrightarrow{EF}$.

3. Draw two parallel rays, $\overrightarrow{IS}$ and $\overrightarrow{NO}$.

4. Draw two intersecting lines, $\overleftrightarrow{MY}$ and $\overleftrightarrow{AN}$.

5. Draw a line segment and a ray, $\overline{PO}$ and $\overrightarrow{LA}$, that intersect.

6. Draw a line, $\overleftrightarrow{PU}$, that is parallel to a ray, $\overrightarrow{RA}$.

Right Angles

Family Note

Our class has been studying intersecting lines and, recently, lines that intersect at right angles. Help your child look for objects that have square corners, or right angles—objects like tables, pictures, the kitchen counter, a book, and so on.

Please return this Home Link to school tomorrow.

SRB
88 89

Find 4 things at home that have right angles (square corners).

Below, describe or draw a picture of each of these things. Bring your descriptions or your pictures to school to add to your Geometry Hunt.

Triangles

Family Note

Your child has been learning about the properties of triangles. Watch your child use a ruler to draw triangles by connecting 3 points with 3 line segments. Then help your child use the ruler to measure the sides of triangles 1–3.

Please return this Home Link to school tomorrow.

SRB
88 89

Show someone at home how to draw triangles. For each problem, connect the 3 points with 3 line segments. Then measure the sides to find out whether triangles 1–3 are correct. If you do not have a ruler at home, cut out and use the ruler at the right.

1. equilateral triangle

A •

• B   • C

All sides and angles are equal.

2. isosceles triangle

D •

• F   • E

Two sides are equal.

3. scalene triangle

•G

I •

•H

No sides are equal.

4. right triangle • K

J •

•L

The triangle has a right angle ($\frac{1}{4}$ turn).

5. obtuse triangle

M •

•O

N •

The triangle has an angle larger than a right angle.

6. acute triangle

P •

•Q

R •

All angles are smaller than a right angle.

15
14
13
12
11
10
9
8
7
6
5
4
3
2
1
0 cm

Quadrangles

Family Note

Help your child complete the statements. A *right angle* is a square corner. *Parallel sides* are sides that are the same distance apart and will never meet, no matter how far they are extended. *Opposite sides* are sides directly across from each other. *Adjacent sides* are sides that meet at a vertex.

Please return this Home Link to school tomorrow.

Fill in using the following terms: **equal   parallel   right angles**

1. Square

All sides are _____ in length.

All angles are _____.

Opposite sides are _____ to each other.

2. Rectangle (Squares are special rectangles.)

All angles are _____.

Pairs of opposite sides are both _____

in length and _____ to each other.

3. Rhombus (Squares are also this shape.)

All sides are _____ in length.

Opposite sides are _____ to each other.

4. Parallelogram (squares and rhombuses included)

Opposite sides are _____ in length.

Opposite sides are _____ to each other.

5. Kite

Adjacent sides, but not opposite sides,

are _____ in length.

Name   Date   Time

Naming Polygons

Home Link 6.6

Family Note

Our class has been naming polygons. Help your child think of names with different numbers of letters, so that he or she can draw and name several different polygons.

Please return this Home Link to school tomorrow.

Think of names that have *different* letters. Use the letters to name points on each circle. Then use a pencil and a straightedge to connect the points to make a polygon. Count the number of sides. Name the polygon.

Example

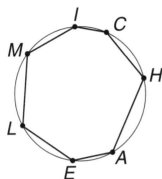

This polygon has ____7____ sides.

This polygon is a *heptagon*.

Its name is ___MICHAEL___.

1.

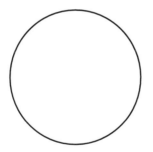

This polygon has _____ sides.

This polygon is a _____.

Its name is _____.

2.

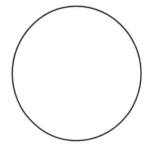

This polygon has _____ sides.

This polygon is a _____.

Its name is _____.

3. Draw more circles and polygons on the back of this paper. Why do you think each letter in a polygon's name can be used only once?_____

Use with Lesson 6.6.

139

**Family
Note**

If your child needs help with the following problems, consider putting up signs
in a room in your house to indicate the directions *north, south, east,* and *west.*
Do the turns with your child. Refer to a clock to help your child determine which
direction is clockwise and which direction is counterclockwise.

Please return this Home Link to school tomorrow.

Make the turns described below. Show which way you face
after each turn.

- Draw a dot on the circle.

- Label the dot with a letter.

Example Face north.

Do a $\frac{1}{2}$ turn counterclockwise.

On the circle, mark the direction
you are facing with the letter *A.*

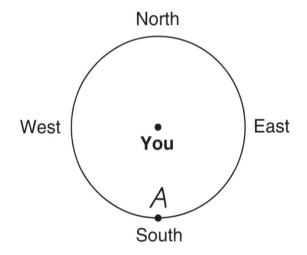

1. Face north. Do a $\frac{1}{4}$ turn clockwise.
Mark the direction you are facing
with the letter *B.*

2. Face north. Do a $\frac{3}{4}$ turn clockwise.
Mark the direction you are facing
with the letter *C.*

3. Face east. Do a $\frac{1}{4}$ turn
counterclockwise. Mark the
direction you are facing with the
letter *D.*

4. Face west. Make less than a $\frac{1}{4}$ turn
clockwise. Mark the direction you
are facing with the letter *E.*

5. Face north. Make more than
a $\frac{1}{2}$ turn clockwise, but less
than a $\frac{3}{4}$ turn clockwise. Mark the
direction you are facing with the
letter *F.*

6. Face north. Make less than a
$\frac{1}{2}$ turn but more than a $\frac{1}{4}$ turn
counterclockwise. Mark the
direction you are facing with the
letter *G.*

Degree Measures

Family Note

Our class has been learning about turns, angles, and angle measures. We have seen that a full turn can be represented by an angle of 360°, a $\frac{1}{2}$ turn by an angle of 180°, a $\frac{1}{4}$ turn by an angle of 90°, and so on. Help your child match the measures below with the angles pictured. It is not necessary to measure the angles with a protractor.

Please return this Home Link to school tomorrow.

Tell which angle has the given measure.

1. about 180°   angle _____

2. about 90°   angle _____

3. about 270°   angle _____

4. between 0° and 90°   angle _____

5. between 90° and 180°   angle _____

Rotation	Degrees
$\frac{1}{4}$ turn	90°
$\frac{1}{2}$ turn	180°
$\frac{3}{4}$ turn	270°
full turn	360°

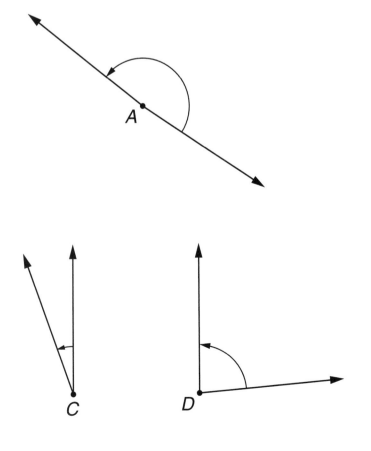

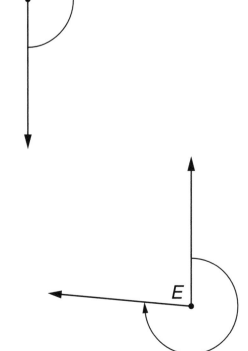

Symmetric Shapes

Family Note

Our class has been studying lines of symmetry—lines that divide figures into matching parts. Help your child look for symmetric shapes in books, newspapers, and magazines, and in objects around the house, such as windows, pieces of furniture, dishes, and so on.

Please return this Home Link to school tomorrow.

1. Fold a sheet of paper in half. Cut off the folded corner, as shown. Before you unfold the cutoff piece, guess its shape.

   a. Unfold the cutoff piece.

      What shape is it? _____

   b. How many sides of the cutoff

      piece are the same length? _____

   c. How many angles are the same size? _____

   d. The fold is a line of symmetry. Does the cutoff

      piece have any other lines of symmetry?_____

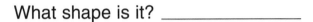

2. Fold a sheet of paper in half. Fold it in half again. Make a mark on both folded edges 2 inches from the folded corner. Cut off the folded corner. Before you unfold the cutoff piece, guess its shape.

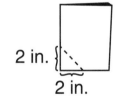

2 in.

2 in.

   a. Unfold the cutoff piece. What shape is it? _____

   b. Are there any other lines of
      symmetry besides the fold lines? _____

   c. Draw a picture of the cutoff shape.
      Draw all its lines of symmetry.

Congruent Figures

Family Note

If your child has difficulty determining the congruent shapes just by looking, encourage her or him to cut out the first shape. Your child can then rotate the shape or flip it to find a congruent shape.

Please return this Home Link to school tomorrow.

Two figures that are exactly the same size and shape are called **congruent** figures. In each of the following, circle the shape or shapes that are congruent to the first shape. Explain to someone at home why the other shape or shapes are *not* congruent to the first.

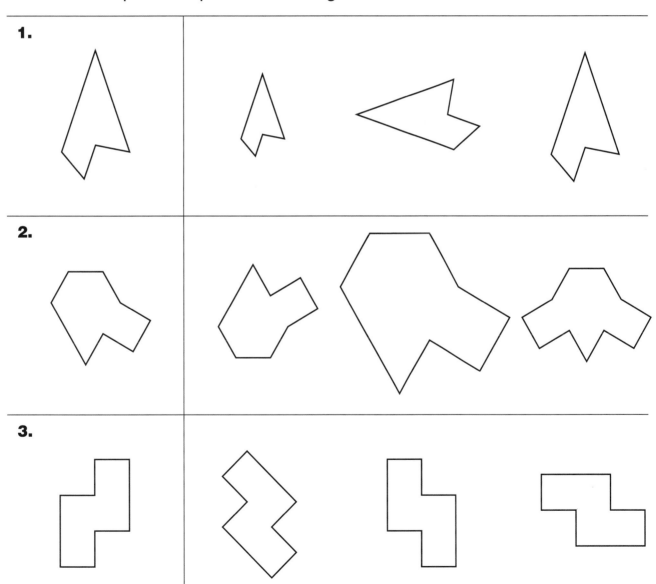

1.

2.

3.

Name   Date   Time

3-Dimensional Shapes

Family Note

Have your child identify 3-dimensional shapes. Then help search for 3-D objects (or pictures of objects) around your home for your child to bring to school. Pages 102–106 in the *Student Reference Book* discuss 3-D shapes.

Please return this Home Link to school tomorrow.

1. Identify the pictures of 3-dimensional shapes below.
   Use these words: *cone, prism, pyramid, cylinder,* and *sphere.*

    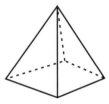

_____   _____   _____   _____   _____

2. Look around your home for objects or pictures of objects that are shaped like cones, prisms, pyramids, cylinders, and spheres. Ask someone at home if you may bring some of the objects or pictures to school to share with the class. Draw or write the names of the shapes you find.

_____

_____

_____

_____

3. Explain to someone at home the differences between 2-dimensional (2-D) and 3-dimensional (3-D) shapes.

  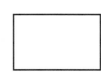 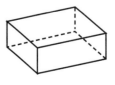

   2-D   3-D   2-D   3-D

Making a Solid Shape

Family Note

Our class has been exploring the characteristics and parts of various 3-dimensional shapes—especially prisms. The pattern on this page can be used to make one of the most familiar types of prisms. Prisms are named for the shapes of their *bases*.

Please return this Home Link to school tomorrow.

SRB
88   89

Cut on the dashed lines. Fold on the dotted lines. Tape or paste each TAB inside or outside the shape.

Discuss the following questions with someone at home:

1. What is this 3-D shape called? _____

2. What is the shape of the base? _____

3. What is the shape of the other faces? _____

4. How many edges does the shape have? _____

5. How many vertices does the shape have? _____

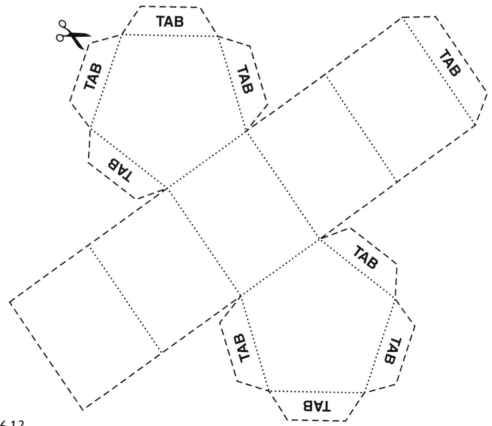

Unit 7: Multiplication and Division

In Unit 7, children will focus on developing automatic recall of the multiplication and division facts. Many of the same strategies that were used in previous grades for addition and subtraction will also be used for multiplication and division.

Children will review multiplication by 0, by 1, and by 10; multiplication facts having square products, such as $5 \times 5 = 25$ and $2 \times 2 = 4$; and the turn-around rule, which shows that $2 \times 5 = 10$ is the same as $5 \times 2 = 10$.

Children will also continue to work with fact families and Fact Triangles as they learn the multiplication and division facts.

$$7 \times 8 = 56$$
$$8 \times 7 = 56$$
$$56 \div 7 = 8$$
$$56 \div 8 = 7$$

Fact family for the
numbers 7, 8, and 56

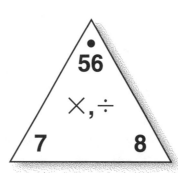

Fact Triangle

The ultimate goal is for children to memorize all the basic arithmetic facts by the end of the year. Please keep in mind that even as your child is making progress, he or she may still experience difficulty with particular facts. Until all facts needed to solve a given problem are memorized, continue to encourage your child to "figure out" an answer by any available means.

Please keep this Family Letter for reference as your child works through Unit 7.

$0 \times 9 = 0$

$2 \times 2 = 4$

$2 \times 1 = 2$

$3 \times 10 = 30$

Vocabulary

Important terms in Unit 7:

factors The numbers being multiplied.

$$4 \times 3 = 12$$

factors ⎯⎯⎯⎯⎯⎯⎯⎯⎯⎯ product

product The result of doing multiplication.

square number A number that is the product of a number multiplied by itself; a number that can be represented by a square array. For example, $5 \times 5 = 25$ forms a square array; therefore, 25 is a square number.

estimate A calculation of a close, rather than an exact, answer; a number close to another number.

array A rectangular arrangement of objects in rows and columns.

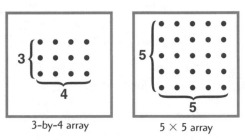

3-by-4 array 5×5 array

multiple of a number The product of that number multiplied by a whole number. For example, 18 is a multiple of 6 because $6 \times 3 = 18$.

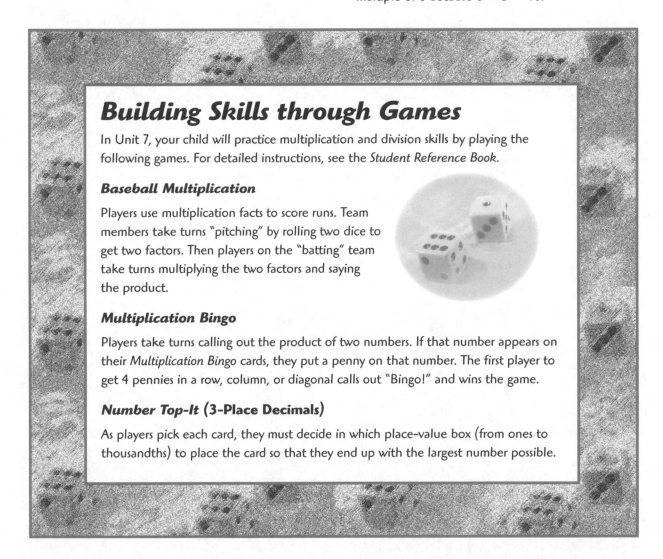

Building Skills through Games

In Unit 7, your child will practice multiplication and division skills by playing the following games. For detailed instructions, see the *Student Reference Book*.

Baseball Multiplication

Players use multiplication facts to score runs. Team members take turns "pitching" by rolling two dice to get two factors. Then players on the "batting" team take turns multiplying the two factors and saying the product.

Multiplication Bingo

Players take turns calling out the product of two numbers. If that number appears on their *Multiplication Bingo* cards, they put a penny on that number. The first player to get 4 pennies in a row, column, or diagonal calls out "Bingo!" and wins the game.

Number Top-It (3-Place Decimals)

As players pick each card, they must decide in which place-value box (from ones to thousandths) to place the card so that they end up with the largest number possible.

Do-Anytime Activities

To work with your child on the concepts taught in this unit and in previous units,
try these interesting and rewarding activities:

1 Practice multiplication facts by playing games and by working with Fact Triangles.

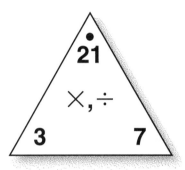

2 Ask your child to count by certain intervals.
For example: "Start at zero and count by 6s."

3 Provide your child with problems with missing factors for multiplication practice.
For example: "6 times what number equals 18?"

4 Ask questions that involve equal sharing.
For example: "Eight children share 64 paperback books.
How many books does each child get?"

5 Ask questions that involve equal groups.
For example: "Pencils are packaged in boxes of 8. There are 3 boxes.
How many pencils are there in all?"

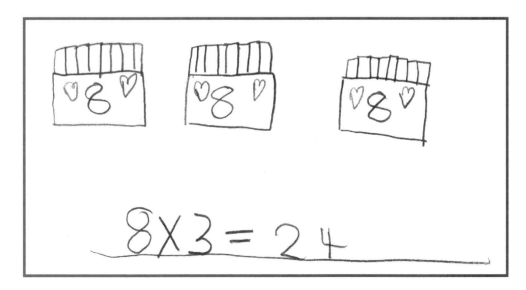

As You Help Your Child with Homework

As your child brings home assignments, you may want to go over the instructions together, clarifying them as necessary. The answers listed below will guide you through this unit's Home Links.

Home Link 7.2

1.

Factor	Factor	Product
3	5	15
7	2	14
4	10	40
8	8	64
9	5	45
4	8	32
864	1	864
10	10	100
0	999	0
1	48	48
7	7	49
243	0	0

Home Link 7.4

1. $(17 - 10) + 3 = 10$ **2.** $17 - (10 + 3) = 4$

3. $(26 - 7) \times 2 = 38$ **4.** $26 - (7 \times 2) = 12$

5. $(24 - 17) - 6 = 1$ **6.** $24 - (17 - 6) = 13$

7. $3 \times (6 + 13) = 57$ **8.** $(3 \times 6) + 13 = 31$

10. The parentheses are placed incorrectly.
The number model should be $(8 \times 4) + 4 = 36$.

Home Link 7.5

Scoring 15 Basketball Points
Possible answers:

Number of 3-point baskets	Number of 2-point baskets	Number of 1-point baskets	Number models
5	0	0	$(5 \times 3) + (0 \times 2) + (0 \times 1) = 15$
0	5	5	$(0 \times 3) + (5 \times 2) + (5 \times 1) = 15$
3	3	0	$(3 \times 3) + (3 \times 2) + (0 \times 1) = 15$
4	0	3	$(4 \times 3) + (0 \times 2) + (3 \times 1) = 15$
2	3	3	$(2 \times 3) + (3 \times 2) + (3 \times 1) = 15$
1	6	0	$(1 \times 3) + (6 \times 2) + (0 \times 1) = 15$

Home Link 7.6

1. $8 \times 200 = 1,600$ **2.** $9 \times 30 = 270$
  $200 \times 8 = 1,600$ $30 \times 9 = 270$
  $1,600 \div 8 = 200$ $270 \div 9 = 30$
  $1,600 \div 200 = 8$ $270 \div 30 = 9$

3. $6 \times 40 = 240$
  $40 \times 6 = 240$
  $240 \div 6 = 40$
  $240 \div 40 = 6$

Home Link 7.7

2. b. 1,750   **c.** 1,251   **f.** 515   **g.** 614
  i. 522

Home Link 7.8

5. a. 1,200 **b.** 1,400 **c.** 400 **d.** 800
  e. 2,000 **f.** 200 **g.** 2,000 **h.** 1,000
  i. 0   Total = 9,000

Sample answers:

6. a. 10×10 **b.** 3×50
  c. 30×3 **d.** 40×4

a	b	
100 +	150	= <u>250</u>
c 90 +	**d** 160	= <u>250</u>

Total
500

Home Link 7.9

Mystery Numbers:

100; 199; 70; 44; 1,000; and 998

Name _____   Date _____   Time _____

Which Way Out?

Home Link 7.1

Family Note

Today your child explored patterns in square products, such as 3 × 3 and 4 × 4. The activity below provides practice in identifying square products. Have your child start at the picture of the Minotaur and use a pencil so he or she can erase wrong turns. If your child finds this activity difficult, suggest that he or she mark each square product before attempting to find a path.

Please return this Home Link to school tomorrow.

According to Greek mythology, there was a monster called the Minotaur that was half bull and half human. The king had a special mazelike dwelling built, from which the Minotaur could not escape. The dwelling, called a **labyrinth** (la bə rinth), had many rooms and passageways that formed a puzzle. Whoever went in could not find the way out without help. One day, a Greek hero, Theseus, decided to slay the monster. To find his way out of the labyrinth, his friend Ariadne gave him a very, very long string of pearls to unwind as he walked through the passageways. After Theseus slew the Minotaur, he followed the string of pearls to escape.

Pretend you are Theseus. To find your way out, you may go through only those rooms numbered with square products. Start at the Minotaur's chambers and draw a path to the exit.

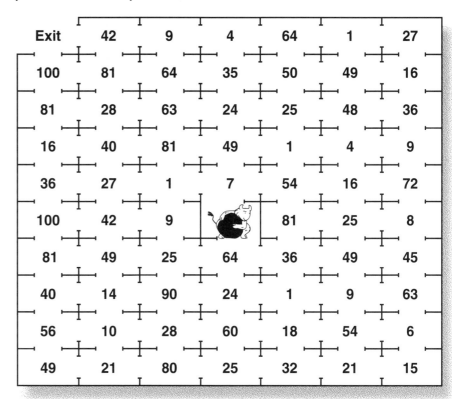

Use with Lesson 7.1.

157

Factors and Products

Family Note

Listen to your child explain what factors and products are before he or she writes the answers in the table. Then listen as your child tells you what he or she knows about multiplying by 1, multiplying by 0, and multiplying square numbers. Fact Triangles for the remaining multiplication/division facts are included with this Home Link.

Please return this Home Link to school tomorrow.

1. Explain to someone at home what factors and products are. Find the missing products and factors in the table.

Factor	Factor	Product
3	5	15
7		14
4	10	
8	8	
9		45
	8	32
864	1	864
10		100
0	999	
	48	48
7	7	
243		0

2. Tell someone what you know about the products when you multiply by 1.

3. Tell someone what you know about the products when you multiply by 0.

4. Tell someone everything you know about facts with square numbers.

Multiplication Bingo (Easy Facts)

Family Note

Today, the class learned to play *Multiplication Bingo*. This game is a good way to practice the multiplication facts. Ask your child to show you how to play the game; then play a couple of games. When your child is ready to practice harder facts, use the cards and list of numbers on the next page. Encourage your child to keep a record of the facts he or she misses.

Materials
- ❏ number cards 1–6 and 10 (4 of each)
- ❏ 8 pennies or other counters for each player
- ❏ game mat for each player

Players   2 or 3

Directions

1. Write each of the following numbers in any order in one of the squares on a game mat: 1, 4, 6, 8, 9, 12, 15, 16, 18, 20, 24, 25, 30, 36, 50, 100.

2. Shuffle the number cards. Place the cards facedown on the table.

3. Take turns. When it is your turn, take the top 2 cards and call out the product of the 2 numbers. If the other players do not agree with your answer, check it using a calculator.

4. If your answer is correct and the product is a number on your grid, place a penny or a counter on that number.

5. If your answer is incorrect, you lose your turn.

6. The first player to get 4 counters in a row, column, diagonal or 8 counters on the game mat, calls out "Bingo!" and wins the game.

   If all the cards are used before someone wins, shuffle the cards again and keep playing.

Multiplication Bingo (All Facts)

Follow the same rules as for *Multiplication Bingo,* with the following exceptions:

- Use a deck of number cards with 4 cards each for the numbers 2–9.

- Write each of the numbers in the list in one of the squares on the grid. Mix them up.

- Don't write the numbers in order.

List of numbers

24	35	48	63
27	36	49	64
28	42	54	72
32	45	56	81

Record the facts you miss. Practice them in your spare time.

_____ _____ _____

_____ _____ _____

_____ _____ _____

Parentheses Puzzles

Family Note

Observe as your child adds parentheses and explains what to do first in the number model in Exercise 1. If your child is unable to write a correct number model for the Challenge problem, ask how many gifts Rivera would need to fill 8 bags and how many she would need to also take care of Denise.

Please return this Home Link to school tomorrow.

Show someone at home how to add parentheses to complete the number models below. Remember that the parentheses are used to show what you do first.

1. $17 - 10 + 3 = 10$

2. $17 - 10 + 3 = 4$

3. $26 - 7 \times 2 = 38$

4. $26 - 7 \times 2 = 12$

5. $24 - 17 - 6 = 1$

6. $24 - 17 - 6 = 13$

7. $3 \times 6 + 13 = 57$

8. $3 \times 6 + 13 = 31$

9. Make up other "parentheses puzzles" below.

_____   _____

_____   _____

Challenge

10. Rivera made 8 party bags for her birthday party. Each bag contained 4 small gifts for her friends. When Denise said she could come, Rivera had to make one more bag with 4 gifts. How many small gifts did Rivera need to fill her bags?

Walter wrote this number model: $8 \times (4 + 4) = 64$
Explain Walter's mistake.

_____

_____

_____

Basketball Math

***Family
Note***

We have been using points scored in basketball to illustrate the use of parentheses in number models. Work with your child to find various combinations of 3-point, 2-point, and 1-point baskets that add up to 15 points. Ask your child to explain what the parentheses in the number models tell you about how to find the answers.

Please return this Home Link to school tomorrow.

Tell someone at home how basketball players can score points with 3-point baskets, 2-point baskets, and 1-point free throws. Find different ways a player can score 15 points.

Scoring 15 Basketball Points

Number of 3-point baskets	Number of 2-point baskets	Number of 1-point baskets	Number models
3	2	2	$(3 \times 3) + (2 \times 2) + (2 \times 1) = 15$

Choose a point total greater than 20. Then find ways to get that point total.

Scoring _____ Basketball Points

Number of 3-point baskets	Number of 2-point baskets	Number of 1-point baskets	Number models

Extended Facts on Triangles

Family Note

Today, the class learned that if you know a basic multiplication fact, such as $4 \times 6 = 24$, you can get the answer to an extended multiplication fact like 40×6 or 4×600. The same approach works for extended division facts like $120 \div 3$ or $1,500 \div 5$. The extended Fact Triangles on this page work the same way as the basic Fact Triangles.

Please return this Home Link to school tomorrow.

Fill in the extended Fact Triangles. Write the fact families.

1.

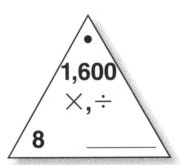

1,600
×,÷
8 _____

_____ × _____ = _____

_____ × _____ = _____

_____ ÷ _____ = _____

_____ ÷ _____ = _____

2.

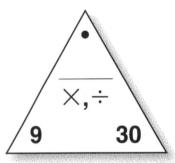

×,÷
9   30

_____ × _____ = _____

_____ × _____ = _____

_____ ÷ _____ = _____

_____ ÷ _____ = _____

3.

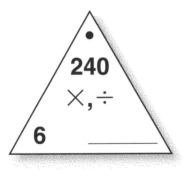

240
×,÷
6 _____

_____ × _____ = _____

_____ × _____ = _____

_____ ÷ _____ = _____

_____ ÷ _____ = _____

4. Write your own.

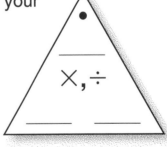

×,÷

_____ × _____ = _____

_____ × _____ = _____

_____ ÷ _____ = _____

_____ ÷ _____ = _____

Estimation

Family Note

Today, we solved problems by making estimates. We emphasized that it is not always necessary to find the exact answer to a problem. For example, when you go to the store, you can estimate whether you have enough money to pay for the items you want to purchase. In most cases, it is not necessary to find the exact cost. The cashier will do that for you.

Please return this Home Link to school tomorrow.

1. An average person uses about 10 pounds of paper per week.
Find some things in your home that weigh about that much.
You can check by using a bath scale.

_____

_____

2. Solve *only* those problems with sums *greater* than 500.

a. 180 + 37	**b.** 1,358 + 392	**c.** 742 + 509
Answer	**Answer**	**Answer**
d. 118 + 292	**e.** 226 + 248	**f.** 357 + 158
Answer	**Answer**	**Answer**
g. 298 + 316	**h.** 195 + 188	**i.** 313 + 209
Answer	**Answer**	**Answer**

A Multiplication Puzzle

Family Note

Practice finding products like 4×70, 900×5, and 30×50 with your child before he or she works the two puzzles.

Please return this Home Link to school tomorrow.

Work with someone at home.

1. Find each product below (for Problems 5a–5i).

2. Record each product in the square labeled with the letter of the problem. For example, write the product for Problem **a** in Box **a**.

3. Add the numbers in each row. Write the sum next to the row.

4. Add these sums and write the answer in the Total box.

5. The number in the Total box should equal $3 \times 3,000$.

   a. 30×40

   b. 20×70

   c. 20×20

   d. 10×80

   e. 40×50

   f. 20×10

   g. 4×500

   h. $10 \times 10 \times 10$

   i. $10,000 \times 0$

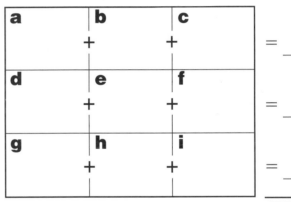

Challenge

6. Make a puzzle of your own so that the number in the Total box is 500.

   a. _____   **b.** _____

   c. _____   **d.** _____

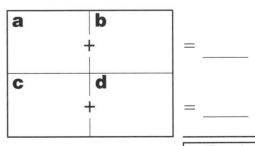

Mystery Numbers

Family Note

Help your child find each missing number by using all the clues. Then help your child create more clues for two other mystery numbers.

Please return this Home Link to school tomorrow.

Find each missing number. Here are your clues.

Greater than	Less than	More clues	Mystery Number
20	101	a 3-digit number	
197	200	an odd number	
67	80	has a zero in the ones place	
40	50	has the same digit in the tens place and the ones place	
917	1,072	has the same digit in the ones, tens, and hundreds places; has 4 digits	
996	1,015	a 3-digit even number	

Make up your own mystery-number puzzles. Write some clues and ask someone to find the numbers.

Greater than	Less than	More clues	Mystery Number

Name   Date   Time

Family Letter

**Home Link
7.10**

Unit 8: Fractions

Unit 8 has two primary objectives:

· to review the uses of fractions and fraction notation

· to help children develop a solid understanding of equivalent fractions,
  or fractions that have the same value

The second objective is especially important, because understanding
equivalent fractions will help children compare fractions and, later,
calculate with fractions.

Children will build their understanding of equivalent fractions by working
with Fraction Cards and name-collection boxes. Fraction Cards are shaded to
show a variety of fractions.

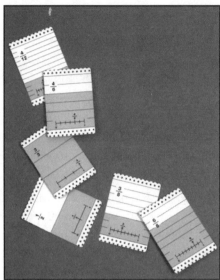

Name-collection boxes contain equivalent names for the same number.
For example, a $\frac{1}{2}$ name-collection box can contain fractions like $\frac{2}{4}$, $\frac{3}{6}$,
and $\frac{4}{8}$, and the decimal 0.50.

Children will also generate lists of equivalent fractions by folding circles
and rectangles into different numbers of equal parts.

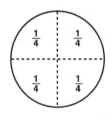 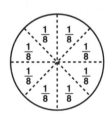

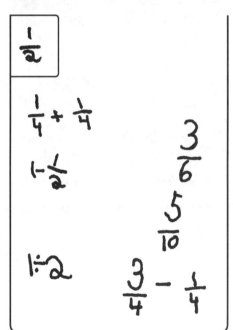

Throughout this unit, children will make up and solve number stories
involving fractions in everyday contexts. They will solve number stories
about collections of real-world objects, such as crayons, books, and cookies.

Finally, children will begin to name quantities greater than 1 with fractions,
such as $\frac{3}{2}$ and $\frac{5}{4}$, and with mixed numbers, such as $2\frac{1}{3}$.

**Please keep this Family Letter for reference as your child works
through Unit 8.**

Use with Lesson 7.10.

Vocabulary

Important terms in Unit 8:

fraction A number in the form $\frac{a}{b}$ used to name part of a whole object or part of a whole collection of objects.

denominator The number of equal parts into which the whole is divided. It is the number written below the bar in a fraction. For example, in the fraction $\frac{3}{4}$, 4 is the denominator.

numerator The number of equal parts of the whole being considered. It is the number written above the bar in a fraction. For example, in the fraction $\frac{3}{4}$, 3 is the numerator.

equivalent fractions Fractions that have different numerators and denominators but name the same amount. For example, $\frac{1}{2}$, $\frac{2}{4}$, $\frac{10}{20}$, and $\frac{5}{10}$ are equivalent fractions.

mixed number A name for a quantity consisting of a whole number and a fraction, such as $2\frac{1}{3}$.

numerator $\dfrac{3}{4}$ ⟵ number of parts shaded
denominator ⟵ number of equal parts

Building Skills through Games

In Unit 8, your child will practice multiplication skills and build his or her understanding of fractions by playing the following games. For detailed instructions, see the *Student Reference Book*.

Baseball Multiplication

Players use multiplication facts to score runs. Team members take turns "pitching" by rolling two dice to get two factors. Then players on the "batting" team take turns multiplying the two factors and saying the product.

Equivalent Fractions Game

Players take turns turning over Fraction Cards and try to find matching cards that show equivalent fractions.

$$\frac{2}{3} \qquad \frac{4}{6}$$

Fraction Top-It

Players turn over two Fraction Cards and compare the shaded parts of the cards. The player with the larger fraction keeps all the cards. The player with more cards at the end wins!

Multiplication Bingo

Players take turns calling out the products of two numbers. If that number appears on their Multiplication Bingo Cards, they put a penny on that number. The first player to get 4 pennies in a row, column, or diagonal calls out "Bingo!" and wins the game.

Use with Lesson 7.10.

Do-Anytime Activities

To work with your child on the concepts taught in this unit and in previous units, try these interesting and rewarding activities:

1 Help your child find fractions in the everyday world—in advertisements, on measuring tools, in recipes, and so on.

2 Count together by a 1-digit number. For example, start at 0 and count by 7s.

3 Dictate 5-, 6-, and 7-digit numbers for your child to write, such as: "thirteen thousand, two hundred forty-seven" (13,247) and "three million, two hundred twenty-nine thousand, eight hundred fifty-six" (3,229,856). Also, write 5-, 6-, and 7- digit numbers for your child to read to you.

4 Practice extended multiplication and division facts, such as $3 \times 7 =$ ___, $30 \times 7 =$ ___, and $300 \times 7 =$ ___; similarly, $18 \div 6 =$ ___, $180 \div 6 =$ ___, and $1,800 \div 6 =$ ___.

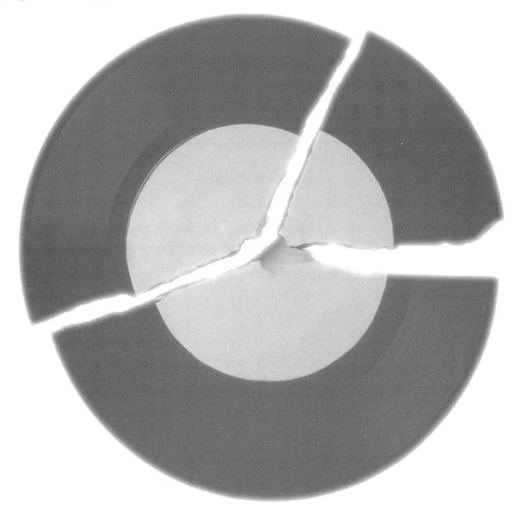

As You Help Your Child with Homework

As your child brings home assignments, you may want to go over the instructions together, clarifying them as necessary. The answers listed below will guide you through this unit's Home Links.

Home Link 8.1

1. $\frac{1}{2}$ $\frac{1}{2}$ **2.** $\frac{1}{4}$ $\frac{1}{4}$ $\frac{1}{4}$ $\frac{1}{4}$ **3.** $\frac{3}{4}$ $\frac{1}{4}$

4. $\frac{5}{7}$ **5.** $\frac{9}{10}$ **6.** $\frac{1}{4}$

7. 0, or $\frac{0}{4}$ **8.** $\frac{3}{4}$ **9.** $\frac{1}{2}$

Home Link 8.2

1. 7 cards **2.** 3 pencils **3.** $\frac{1}{4}$, or $\frac{10}{40}$ **4.** $\frac{1}{5}$, or $\frac{10}{50}$

5. ○○○○○○○⟨○○○○○○○○○○○⟩

6. ⊗⊗⊗⊗⊗⊗⊗⊗⊗○○○

Home Link 8.3

1. $\frac{1}{2}$; $\frac{1}{1}$; $\frac{1}{4}$

2. 9 pieces of fruit are shown.

$\frac{4}{9}$ of the fruit are bananas.

$\frac{2}{9}$ of the fruit are pears.

$\frac{3}{9}$ of the fruit are apples.

$\frac{0}{9}$ of the fruit are oranges.

3.

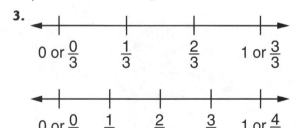

Home Link 8.4

4. $\frac{2}{4}$; $\frac{1}{2}$ **5.** $\frac{3}{6}$; $\frac{1}{2}$ **6.** $\frac{4}{8}$; $\frac{1}{2}$

8. 4 cats **9.** $\frac{4}{16}$

10.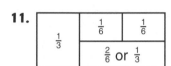

11.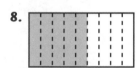

Home Link 8.5

1. 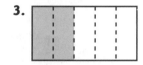 **2.**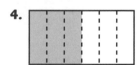

3. 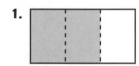 **4.**

5. 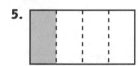 **6.**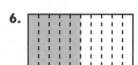

7. **8.**

9. $\frac{2}{3}$, $\frac{7}{8}$, $\frac{5}{9}$ **10.** $\frac{3}{6}$, $\frac{5}{10}$ **11.** > **12.** <

13. > **14.** = **15.** > **16.** <

17. < **18.** =

Home Link 8.6

1. 6; $\frac{6}{4}$; $1\frac{2}{4}$ **2.** 9; $\frac{9}{5}$; $1\frac{4}{5}$ **3.** 7; $\frac{7}{3}$; $2\frac{1}{3}$

4. $\frac{1}{12}$ **5.** $\frac{28}{12}$; $2\frac{4}{12}$

Home Link 8.7

1. 8 eggs **2.** $\frac{1}{4}$ of the lawn

3. 2 miles **4.** $1\frac{1}{4}$ trays

5. 6 quarters; $2.28

Fractions All Around

Family Note

Help your child understand the idea of ONE and fractions of objects and sets. Help your child look for objects or pictures that have fractions or decimals on them.

Please return this Home Link to school tomorrow.

Each square flag below represents ONE. Write the fractions that name each region inside each flag.

1. 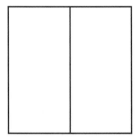   **2.** 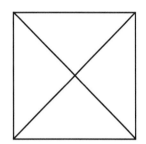   **3.**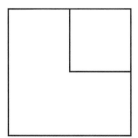

Write a fraction for each picture.

4. 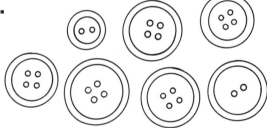   **5.**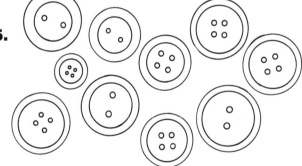

_____ of the buttons have 4 holes.   _____ of the buttons are large.

Write one of the following to tell how full each glass is: 0, $\frac{0}{4}$, $\frac{1}{4}$, $\frac{1}{2}$, or $\frac{3}{4}$ full.

 6. **7.** **8.** **9.**

_____ full glass   _____   _____

Look for things around your house that have fractions or decimals on them. Examples are recipes, measuring cups, wrenches, labels on packages, and pictures in newspapers. Get permission to bring some of them to school for a couple of weeks. We'll put them in our Fractions Museum.

Fraction Number Stories

Family Note

Your child may benefit from modeling the number stories with pennies or counters. Help your child think about the stories as stories about equal shares or equal groups.

Please return this Home Link to school tomorrow.

Solve each problem. Tell someone at home how you did it.
Draw a picture on the back if it will help.

1. Lucy was playing a card game with 2 friends.
   They were playing with a deck of 21 cards.
   Lucy dealt $\frac{1}{3}$ of the deck to each person.
   How many cards did Lucy get? _____ cards

2. Jonathan bought 12 pencils. He gave $\frac{1}{2}$ of them to his brother
   and $\frac{1}{4}$ of them to his friend Mike.
   How many pencils did he give to Mike? _____ pencils

3. Gerard was reading a book with 40 pages.
   He read 10 pages in an hour.
   What fraction of the book did he read in an hour? _____

4. Melissa was reading a book with 50 pages.
   She read 10 pages in an hour.
   What fraction of the book did she read in an hour? _____

Follow the instructions below.

5. Draw 15 small circles. Draw a large circle around $\frac{3}{5}$ of them.

6. Draw 12 small circles. Put an X through $\frac{3}{4}$ of them.

Fraction Puzzles

Family Note

We have been working with fractions of regions and fractions of sets a lot this year. Ask your child to explain how he or she knows which fractions to write in Problems 1 and 2. Today we began to think of fractions on a number line. Ask your child to explain how he or she knows how to fill in the missing numbers on the number lines in Problem 3. If your child seems confused about this, count the number of intervals from 0 to 1 in order to figure out which fraction each small mark indicates. Also, please help your child find more objects labeled with fractions or decimals.

Please return this Home Link to school tomorrow.

1. The first figure is $\frac{3}{4}$ of the whole. What fraction of the *same* whole is each of the other figures? Write the fraction inside the figure.

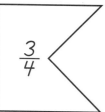 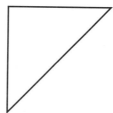  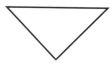

2. How many pieces of fruit are shown? _____

     _____ of the fruit are bananas.

     _____ of the fruit are pears.

     _____ of the fruit are apples.

What fraction of the fruit are oranges?

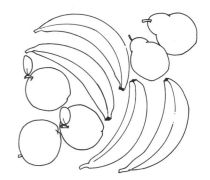

3. Fill in the missing numbers on each number line.

<!-- number lines -->

0 or $\frac{0}{3}$ ____ ____ 1 or $\frac{3}{3}$ 0 or $\frac{0}{4}$ ____ ____ ____ 1 or $\frac{4}{4}$

4. Continue to look for items and pictures that have fractions or decimals on them. Get permission to bring them to school for the Fractions Museum.

Equivalent Fractions

Family Note

The class continues fraction work by finding equivalent names for fractions. Different fractions that name the same amount are called equivalent fractions. The fractions that complete Problems 4–6 are equivalent. Help your child name the fractional parts in these problems. Ask your child to explain the fraction name she or he chose in Problem 9—a fraction that is equivalent to $\frac{1}{4}$ and describes the fraction of cats circled.

Please return this Home Link to school tomorrow.

The pictures show three kinds of pie. Use a straightedge to do the following:

1. Divide the peach pie into 4 equal pieces. Shade 2 of the pieces.

2. Divide the blueberry pie into 6 equal pieces. Shade 3 of the pieces.

3. Divide the cherry pie into 8 equal pieces. Shade 4 of the pieces.

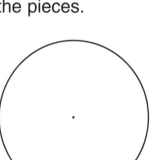

peach pie

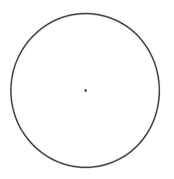

blueberry pie

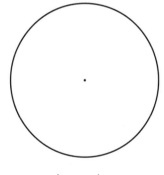

cherry pie

What fraction of each pie did you shade?

4. I shaded ___ of the peach pie.
Write another name for this fraction:

5. I shaded ___ of the blueberry pie.
Write another name for this fraction:

6. I shaded ___ of the cherry pie.
Write another name for this fraction:

Use with Lesson 8.4.

7. Circle $\frac{1}{4}$ of the cats.

8. How many cats did you circle? _____

9. Write a fraction that describes the group of cats you circled, and that is equivalent to $\frac{1}{4}$.

Each whole rectangle below is ONE. Write a fraction inside each part.

10.

$\frac{1}{4}$ · — · —

—

11.

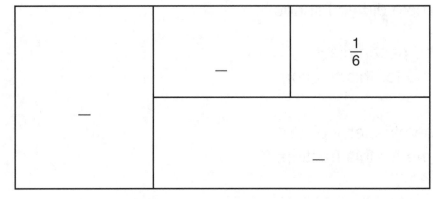

Comparing Fractions with $\frac{1}{2}$

 Family Note

Your child's class is comparing fractions—first, to determine whether they are larger, smaller, or equal to $\frac{1}{2}$. Ask your child to explain how to tell which category a fraction fits into. For more on this topic, see *Student Reference Book* pages 31 and 32.

Please return this Home Link to school tomorrow.

SRB
31 32

Shade each rectangle to match the fraction below it. *Example* $\frac{2}{4}$

1.

$\frac{2}{3}$

2.

$\frac{3}{8}$

3.

$\frac{2}{5}$

4.

$\frac{3}{6}$

5.

$\frac{1}{4}$

6.

$\frac{5}{10}$

7.

$\frac{7}{8}$

8.

$\frac{5}{9}$

9. List the fractions above that are greater than $\frac{1}{2}$. _____

10. List the fractions above that are equal to $\frac{1}{2}$. _____

Insert $<$, $>$, or $=$ in each problem below.

11. $\frac{6}{8}$ _____ $\frac{1}{2}$ **12.** $\frac{2}{9}$ _____ $\frac{1}{2}$

13. $\frac{10}{12}$ _____ $\frac{1}{2}$ **14.** $\frac{6}{12}$ _____ $\frac{1}{2}$

> $<$ means *is less than*
> $>$ means *is greater than*
> $=$ means *is equal to*

Challenge

Insert $<$, $>$, or $=$ in each problem. On the back of this page, explain how you solved these problems.

15. $\frac{10}{16}$ _____ $\frac{1}{2}$ **16.** $\frac{7}{20}$ _____ $\frac{1}{2}$ **17.** $\frac{15}{75}$ _____ $\frac{1}{2}$ **18.** $\frac{20}{40}$ _____ $\frac{1}{2}$

Fractions and Mixed Numbers

Family Note

Today the class began looking at fractions greater than 1 and mixed numbers. So far, we have been working with area models (shaded areas) for these numbers. The Challenge problem asks about fractions of a set. The *whole* is a dozen eggs, so each egg is $\frac{1}{12}$ of the whole. Have your child explain how he or she figured out what the fraction and mixed number should be for the egg-carton drawings.

Please return this Home Link to school tomorrow.

1.

How many fourths? _____ fourths   Color 6 fourths.

Write the fraction: Write the mixed number: _____

2.

How many fifths? _____ fifths   Color 9 fifths.

Write the fraction: Write the mixed number: _____

3.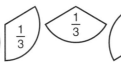

How many thirds? _____ thirds   Color 7 thirds.

Write the fraction: Write the mixed number: _____

Fractions/Mixed Numbers (cont.)

Challenge

4.

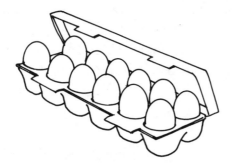

What fraction of the WHOLE carton is each egg?

5.

Write the fraction: Write the mixed number: _____

Use with Lesson 8.6.

Fraction Number Stories

Family Note

In class we have been solving all kinds of fraction number stories. If some of these Home Link problems seem difficult, encourage your child to model them with pennies or draw pictures to help solve them.

Please return this Home Link to school tomorrow.

Solve these fraction stories. Use pennies, counters, or pictures to help.

1. Lisa bought a dozen eggs. She dropped her bag on the way home, and $\frac{2}{3}$ of the eggs broke. How many eggs broke? _____ eggs

2. Roger mowed $\frac{3}{4}$ of the lawn before lunch.
   What fraction of the lawn did he have to finish after lunch? _____ of the lawn

3. Missy lives 1 mile from school. One day, she had walked $\frac{1}{2}$ of the way when she remembered she had to return a book to the library. She went home to get it. Then she walked to school. How far did she walk in all? _____ miles

4. Sid made 4 trays of cookies. He took 2 trays to school for his birthday. He gave another $\frac{3}{4}$ of a tray of cookies to his teacher. How many trays of cookies did Sid have left? _____ trays

Challenge

5. Robert found 24 coins. $\frac{1}{3}$ of them were pennies, $\frac{1}{4}$ were nickels, $\frac{1}{6}$ were dimes, and the rest were quarters.

   How many were quarters? _____

   How much money had he found all together? $_____

   Explain how you got your answers.

   _____

   _____

   _____

Unit 9: **Multiplication and Division**

In Unit 9, children will develop a variety of strategies for multiplying whole numbers. They will begin by using mental math (computation done by counting fingers, drawing pictures, and making diagrams, as well as by computing in one's head). Later in this unit, children will be introduced to two specific algorithms, or methods, for multiplication: the partial-products algorithm and the lattice method.

Partial-Products Algorithm

The partial-products algorithm is a variation of the traditional multiplication algorithm that most adults learned as children. Note that the multiplication is done from left to right and emphasizes place value in the numbers being multiplied.

```
           28
         ×  4
```
Multiply 4 × 20.   →   80   First, calculate 4 [20s].
Multiply 4 × 8.   →   + 32   Then calculate 4 [8s].
Add the two partial products. → 112   Finally, add the two partial products.

It is important that when children verbalize this method, they understand and say "4 [20s]," not "4 × 2." In doing so, they gain a better understanding of the magnitude of numbers along with better number sense.

```
          379
        ×   4
```
Multiply 4 × 300.   →   1200   First, calculate 4 [300s].
Multiply 4 × 70.   →   280   Second, calculate 4 [70s].
Multiply 4 × 9.   →   + 36   Then calculate 4 [9s].
Add the three partial products.→ 1516   Finally, add the three partial products.

Check that when your child is verbalizing this strategy, he or she says "4 [300s]," not "4 × 3," and "4 [70s]," not "4 × 7." Using this strategy will also help to reinforce your child's facility with the basic multiplication facts and their extensions.

Lattice Method

Third Grade Everyday Mathematics introduces the lattice method of multiplication for several reasons: This algorithm is historically interesting; it provides practice with multiplication facts and addition of 1-digit numbers; and it is fun. Also, some children find it easier to use than other methods of multiplication.

$$\begin{array}{r} 79 \\ \times\ 4 \\ \hline 316 \end{array}$$

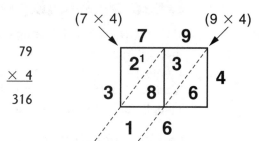

Step 1 Write the factors on the outside of the lattice.

Step 2 Multiply each digit in one factor by each digit in the other factor.

Step 3 Write each product in one small box; ones place digits in the bottom-right half; tens place digits in the upper-left half. When the product is a single-digit answer, write a zero in the upper-left half.

Step 4 Add the numbers inside the lattice along each diagonal. If the sum on a diagonal exceeds 9, add the excess 10s in the next diagonal.

The lattice method and the partial-products algorithm help prepare children for a division algorithm they will learn in fourth grade. Children will choose the algorithms that work best for them.

Also in this unit, children will...

· Write and solve multiplication and division number stories involving multiples of 10, 100, and 1,000.

· Solve division number stories and interpret the remainders.

· Increase their understanding of positive and negative numbers.

Vocabulary

Important terms in Unit 9:

algorithm A step-by-step set of instructions for doing something—carrying out a calculation, solving a problem, and so on.

percent, % Per hundred; times $\frac{1}{100}$; times 0.01; 1 one-hundredth. For example, 15% means $\frac{15}{100}$ or 0.15 or 15 one-hundredths.

degree Celsius (°C) A unit for measuring temperature on the Celsius scale. 0°Celsius is the freezing point of water. 100°Celsius is the boiling point of water.

degree Fahrenheit (°F) A unit for measuring temperature on the Fahrenheit scale. 32°F is the freezing point of water. 212°F is the boiling point of water.

negative number A number less than or below zero; a number to the left of zero on a number line.

factor of a number N A whole number that can be multiplied by another whole number, so that the product is the number N. For example, 12 is a factor of 60, because $5 \times 12 = 60$. Alternatively, a factor of N is a whole number that divides N evenly (without a remainder); for example, 12 is a factor of 60, because $60 \div 12 = 5$.

Use with Lesson 8.8.

Do-Anytime Activities

To work with your child on the concepts taught in this unit and in previous units, try these interesting and rewarding activities:

1 As the class proceeds through the unit, give your child multiplication problems related to the lessons covered, such as 9×23, 3×345, 20×65, and 43×56.

2 Continue to work on multiplication and division facts by using Fact Triangles and fact families, or by playing games.

3 Play *Baseball Multiplication, Factor Bingo,* and other games described in the *Student Reference Book.*

4 Write decimals for your child to read, such as 0.82 (eighty-two hundredths); 0.7 (seven tenths); 0.348 (three hundred forty-eight thousandths); and so on. Ask your child to identify digits in various places—the tenths place, hundredths place, thousandths place.

5 Practice extended multiplication and division facts, such as $3 \times 7 = ?$, $3 \times 70 = $ __, and $3 \times 700 = $ __; $18 \div 6 = $ __, $180 \div 6 = $ __, and $1,800 \div 6 = $ __.

As You Help Your Child with Homework

As your child brings home assignments, you may want to go over the instructions together, clarifying them as necessary. The answers listed below will guide you through this unit's Home Links.

Home Link 9.2

1. 56; 56; 560; 560; 7 [8s] in 56; 70 [8s] in 560; 8 [7s] in 56; 8 [70s] in 560

2. 63; 63; 630; 630; 7 [9s] in 63; 70 [9s] in 630; 9 [7s] in 63; 9 [70s] in 630

3. 40; 40; 400; 400; 50 [8s] in 400; 50 [80s] in 4,000; 8 [50s] in 400; 80 [50s] in 4,000

Home Link 9.3

1. 7 raccoons   **2.** 500 lb   **3.** 100 foxes

4. 600 lb   **5.** 400 lb   **6.** 60 beluga whales

Home Link 9.4

1. 93   **2.** 375   **3.** 765

4. 258   **5.** 1,134

Home Link 9.5

1. yes; $0.79 x 7 = $5.53

2. $12.72; $2.12 x 6 = $12.72

3. $0.90; Sample answer: 10 cards is $6.00 times 2. Compare that with $1.29 times 10. Then subtract to find the difference.

4. pack of 10; $0.55; Sample answer: Compare $0.55 times 8 with $3.85. Then subtract to find the difference.

Home Link 9.6

1 row: yes; 18 chairs   **7 rows:** no; 0 chairs

2 rows: yes; 9 chairs   **8 rows:** no; 0 chairs

3 rows: yes; 6 chairs   **9 rows:** yes; 2 chairs

4 rows: no; 0 chairs   **10 rows:** no; 0 chairs

5 rows: no; 0 chairs   **18 rows:** yes; 1 chair

6 rows: yes; 3 chairs   1; 18; 2; 9; 3; 6

Family Letter, *continued*

Home Link 9.7

1. a. 1 $10 bill   **b.** 9 $1 bills

   c. 1 $1 bill left over   **d.** $0.25   **e.** $19.25

   f. $77.00 ÷ 4 = $19.25

2. a. 2 $10 bills   **b.** 1 $1 bill

   c. 2 $10 bills left over   **d.** $0.66   **e.** $21.66

   f. $65.00 ÷ 3 = $21.66 R2¢

Home Link 9.8

1. 8 tables with 1 empty chair

2. 7 cartons with 1 egg left over

3. 10 packs with 7 extra markers

4. 5 candy bars with 1 left over

5. 12 packages of buns with 6 buns left over

Home Link 9.9

1. 92

2. 415

3. 822

4. 7,248

Home Link 9.10

1. 171

2. 364

3. 1,632

4. 4,320

Home Link 9.11

1. 760   **2.** 850   **3.** 5,580

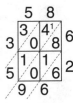

4. 1,120   **5.** 2,100

Home Link 9.12

1. 735   **2.** 731   **3.** 3,596

4. 2,695   **5.** 3,003

Home Link 9.13

1. −40°F; −40°C   **2.** 220°F; 104°C

3. 10°C   **4.** 18° colder

5. yes; no; It would be about 86°F outside.

6. yes; no; Water freezes at 0°C, so it would be cold enough to ice skate.

Use with Lesson 8.8.

Multiplication Facts

Family Note

Use a clock or watch that shows seconds to time your child as he or she completes one row of multiplication facts at a time. Then review facts that need practice.

Please return this Home Link to school tomorrow.

Ask someone at home to time you. For each Fact Minute below, do as many problems as you can in that minute.

Fact Minute 1

4	3	7	4	2	5	6	5	3	2
× 2	× 6	× 2	× 4	× 8	× 6	× 6	× 4	× 7	× 5

Fact Minute 2

2	5	3	7	4	3	4	5	6	4
× 3	× 7	× 8	× 7	× 8	× 9	× 6	× 5	× 8	× 9

Fact Minute 3

2	4	6	8	6	2	9	7	4	8
× 7	× 5	× 3	× 4	× 7	× 9	× 4	× 5	× 7	× 3

Fact Minute 4

4	8	9	7	5	9	8	7	6	8
× 3	× 8	× 5	× 4	× 9	× 6	× 2	× 6	× 9	× 6

Ask the person who timed you to check your answers. List on the back the facts you missed and the facts you did not complete. These are the facts you need to practice.

Multiplication Facts and Extensions

>
>
> **Family Note**
>
> Help your child practice multiplication facts and their extensions. Observe as your child creates fact extensions, demonstrating further understanding of multiplication.
>
> *Please return this Home Link to school tomorrow.*

Solve each problem.

1. a. 8 [7s] = _____ or 8 × 7 = _____

 b. 8 [70s] = _____ or 8 × 70 = _____

 c. How many 8s in 56? _____   **d.** How many 8s in 560? _____

 e. How many 7s in 56? _____   **f.** How many 70s in 560? _____

2. a. 9 [7s] = _____ or 9 × 7 = _____

 b. 9 [70s] = _____ or 9 × 70 = _____

 c. How many 9s in 63? _____   **d.** How many 9s in 630? _____

 e. How many 7s in 63? _____   **f.** How many 70s in 630? _____

3. a. 8 [5s] = _____ or 8 × 5 = _____

 b. 8 [50s] = _____ or 8 × 50 = _____

 c. How many 8s in 400? _____   **d.** How many 80s in 4,000? _____

 e. How many 50s in 400? _____   **f.** How many 50s in 4,000? _____

4. Write a multiplication fact you are trying to learn.
 Then use your fact to write some fact extensions like those above.

_____

_____

_____

_____

Multiplication Number Stories

Family Note

Your child's class is beginning to solve multidigit multiplication and division problems. Although we have practiced multiplication and division with multiples of 10, we have been doing most of our calculating mentally. Encourage your child to explain a solution strategy for each of the problems below.

Please return this Home Link to school tomorrow.

1. How many 30-pound raccoons would weigh about as much as a 210-pound harp seal? _____

2. How much would an alligator weigh if it weighed 10 times as much as a 50-pound sea otter? _____

3. How many 20-pound Arctic foxes would weigh about as much as a 2,000-pound beluga whale? _____

4. Each porcupine weighs 30 pounds. A black bear weighs as much as 20 porcupines.
How much does the black bear weigh? _____

5. A bottle-nosed dolphin could weigh twice as much as a 200-pound common dolphin.
How much could the bottle-nosed dolphin weigh? _____

Challenge

6. How many 2,000-pound beluga whales would weigh as much as one 120,000-pound right whale? _____

Name   Date   Time

The Partial-Products Algorithm

Home Link
9.4

Family Note

Today the class began working with our first formal procedure for multiplication—the *partial-products algorithm*. Children who master this algorithm have a good understanding of the concept of multidigit multiplication. Encourage your child to explain this algorithm to you.

Please return this Home Link to school tomorrow.

SRB
58 59

Use the partial-products algorithm to solve these problems:

Example	**1.**
46 × 7 7 [40s]→ 280 7 [6s]→ + 42 280 + 42→ 322	31 × 3
2. 75 × 5	**3.** 85 × 9
4. 43 × 6	**5.** 162 × 7

Use with Lesson 9.4.

205

Saving at the Stock-Up Sale

**Family
Note**

Today the class used mental math and the partial-products algorithm to solve shopping problems. Note that for some of the problems below, an estimate will answer the question. For others, an exact answer is needed. If your child is able to make the calculations mentally, encourage him or her to explain the solution strategy to you.

Please return this Home Link to school tomorrow.

Decide whether you will need to estimate or calculate an exact answer to solve each problem below. Then solve the problem. Record the answer and write a number model (or models) to show how you found the answer.

1. Phil has $6.00. He wants to buy Creepy Creature erasers. They cost $1.05 each. If he buys more than 5, they are $0.79 each. Does he have enough money to buy 7 Creepy Creature erasers? _____

   Number model: _____

2. Mrs. Katz is buying cookies for a school party. The cookies cost $2.48 per dozen. If she buys more than 4 dozen, they cost $2.12 per dozen. How much are 6 dozen? _____

   Number model: _____

3. Baseball cards are on sale for $1.29 per card, or 5 cards for $6. Marty bought 10 cards. How much did he save with the special price? _____
   On the back of this page, explain how you found your answer.

4. Ursula buys 8 pencils. They are $0.55 each, or $3.85 for a package of 10. Which is cheaper—8 pencils or the package of 10 pencils? _____

   How much would she save? _____

   On the back of this page, explain how you found your answer.

Arrays and Factors

Family Note

Discuss with your child all the ways to arrange 18 chairs in equal rows. Then help your child use this information to list the factors of 18 (pairs of numbers whose product is 18).

Please return this Home Link to school tomorrow.

Work with someone at home.

The third grade class is putting on a play. Children have invited 18 people. Gilda and Harvey are in charge of arranging the 18 chairs. They want to arrange them in rows with the same number of chairs in each row, with no chairs left over.

Yes or no: Can they arrange the chairs in ...	If yes, how many chairs in each row?
1 row? _____	_____ chairs
2 rows? _____	_____ chairs
3 rows? _____	_____ chairs
4 rows? _____	_____ chairs
5 rows? _____	_____ chairs
6 rows? _____	_____ chairs
7 rows? _____	_____ chairs
8 rows? _____	_____ chairs
9 rows? _____	_____ chairs
10 rows? _____	_____ chairs
18 rows? _____	_____ chairs

List all the factors of the number 18. (*Hint:* 18 has exactly 6 factors.)

_____ _____ _____

_____ _____ _____

How does knowing all the ways to arrange 18 chairs in equal rows help you find all the factors of 18? Tell someone at home.

_____

_____

_____

_____

Sharing Money with Friends

Family Note

In class we have begun to think about division, but we have not yet introduced a procedure for division. We will work with formal division algorithms in *Fourth Grade Everyday Mathematics.* Encourage your child to solve the following problems in his or her own way and to explain the strategy to you. These problems provide an opportunity to develop a sense of what division means and how it works. Sometimes it helps to model problems with pennies, beans, or other counters that stand for bills and coins.

Please return this Home Link to school tomorrow.

1. $77 is shared equally by 4 friends.

    a. How many $10 bills does each friend get? _____

    b. How many $1 bills does each friend get? _____

    c. How many $1 bills are left over? _____

    d. If the leftover money is shared equally, how many cents does each friend get? _____

    e. Each friend gets a total of $_____

    f. Number model: _____

2. $65 is shared equally by 3 friends.

    a. How many $10 bills does each friend get? _____

    b. How many $1 bills does each friend get? _____

    c. How many $1 bills are left over? _____

    d. If the leftover bills are shared equally, how many cents does each friend get? _____

    e. Each friend gets a total of $_____

    f. Number model: _____

Equal Shares and Equal Parts

Family Note

As the class continues to investigate division, we are looking at remainders and what they mean. The focus of this assignment is on figuring out what to do with the remainder, NOT on using a division algorithm. It is fine to use a calculator because it will not solve the problems. Encourage your child to use counters or draw pictures to help solve difficult problems.

Please return this Home Link to school tomorrow.

Solve the problems below. Remember that you will have to decide what the remainder means in order to answer the questions. You may use your calculator, counters, or pictures to help you solve the problems.

1. There are 31 children in Alice's class. Each table in the classroom seats 4 children. How many tables are needed to seat all of the children?

   _____

2. Gus and June live on a chicken farm. On Tuesday, the hens laid a total of 85 eggs. How many cartons of a dozen eggs can they fill?

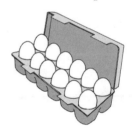

   _____

3. Mrs. Lane is buying markers for a scout project. She needs 93 markers. Markers come in packs of 10. How many packs must she buy?

   _____

Challenge

4. Clem is buying hotdog buns for the class picnic. The class already has 9 packages of hot dogs with 10 in each package. The buns come in packs of 8. How many packs of buns will he have to buy?

   _____

Multiplication Two Ways, Part I

Family Note

Observe as your child solves these problems. See if your child can use more than one method of multiplication, and find out which method your child prefers. Both methods are discussed in the *Student Reference Book,* pages 58–63.

Please return this Home Link to school tomorrow.

SRB
58–63

Use both the lattice method and the partial-products algorithm.

1. 2 × 46 = _____

    4   6

             2

        46
     × 2

2. 5 × 83 = _____

    8   3

             5

        83
     × 5

3. 3 × 274 = _____

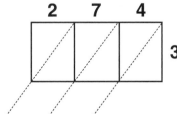

      274
    ×   3

4. 8 × 906 = _____

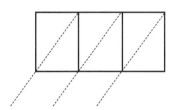

      906
    ×   8

Multiplication Two Ways, Part 2

Family Note

The class continues to practice both the partial-products algorithm and the lattice method. Encourage your child to try these problems in both ways and to compare the answers to be sure that they are correct.

Please return this Home Link to school tomorrow.

Use both the lattice method and the partial-products algorithm.

1. 3 × 57 = _____

```
  5   7
┌───┬───┐
│ ╱ │ ╱ │ 3
└───┴───┘
 ╱   ╱
```

```
  57
×  3
────
```

2. 4 × 91 = _____

```
  9   1
┌───┬───┐
│ ╱ │ ╱ │ 4
└───┴───┘
 ╱   ╱
```

```
  91
×  4
────
```

3. 8 × 204 = _____

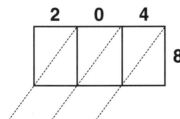

```
 204
×   8
─────
```

4. 9 × 480 = _____

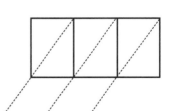

```
 480
×   9
─────
```

2-Digit Multiplication: Two Ways

Family Note

Your child's class continues to practice both the partial-products algorithm and the lattice method, now with 2-digit numbers and 2-digit multiples of 10.

Please return this Home Link to school tomorrow.

Use both the lattice method and the partial-products algorithm.

1. 20 × 38 = _____ | **2.** 50 × 17 = _____ | **3.** 90 × 62 = _____

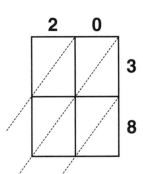

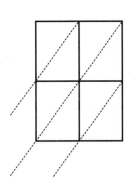

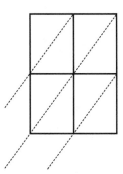

On the back of this page, use your favorite method to solve these problems.

4. 40 × 28 = _____   **5.** 60 × 35 = _____

2 Digits × 2 Digits

Family Note

The class continues to practice both the partial-products algorithm and the lattice method, now with any 2-digit numbers. Encourage your child to try these problems in both ways and to compare the answers to be sure that they are correct.

Please return this Home Link to school tomorrow.

Use both the lattice method and the partial-products algorithm.

1. 21 × 35 = _____

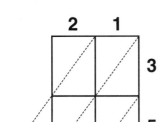

2. 17 × 43 = _____

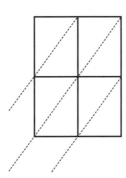

3. 58 × 62 = _____

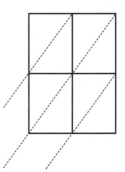

On the back of this page, use your favorite method to solve these problems.

4. 55 × 49 = _____

5. 91 × 33 = _____

Positive and Negative Temperatures

Family Note

Encourage your child to use the thermometer pictured here to answer questions about thermometer scales, temperature changes, and temperature comparisons. If you have a real thermometer, try to show your child how the mercury moves up and down.

Please return this Home Link to school tomorrow.

1. What is the coldest temperature this thermometer could show?

   a. _____°F   **b.** _____°C

2. What is the warmest temperature this thermometer could show?

   a. _____°F   **b.** _____°C

3. What temperature is 20 degrees warmer than −10°C? _____

4. How much colder is −9°C than 9°C? _____

5. Would 30°C be a good temperature for swimming outside? _____

   For sledding? _____ Explain.

   _____

   _____

6. Would −15°C be a good temperature for ice skating? _____

   For inline skating? _____ Explain.

   _____

   _____

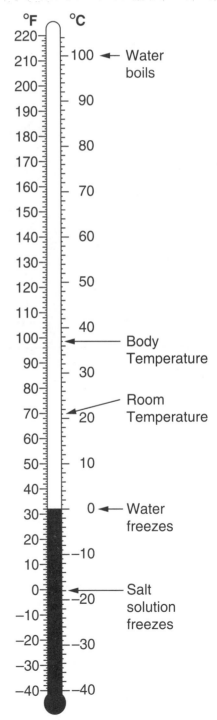

Unit 10: Measurement

This unit has three main objectives:

· To review and extend previous work with measures of length, weight, and capacity
by providing a variety of hands-on activities and applications. These activities will
provide children with experience using both U.S. customary and metric units of
measurement.

· To extend previous work with the median and mode of a set of data and to
introduce the mean (average) of a set of data.

· To introduce two new topics: finding the volume of rectangular prisms and using
ordered pairs to locate points on a coordinate grid.

Children will repeat the personal measurements they made earlier in the year so that
they may record their own growth. They will display these data in graphs and tables and
find typical values for the class by finding the median, mean, and mode of the data.

They will begin to work with volumes of rectangular boxes, which have regular shapes,
and will also compare the volumes of several irregular objects and investigate whether
there is a relationship between the weight of these objects and their volumes.

Please keep this Family Letter for reference as your child works through Unit 10.

Vocabulary

Important terms in Unit 10:

coordinate grid A device for locating points in a plane. It is formed by drawing two number lines at right angles to each other and intersecting at their zero points.

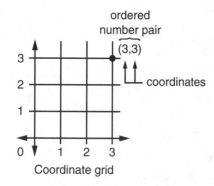

Coordinate grid

coordinates Ordered pairs of numbers written within parentheses and used to locate points on a coordinate grid.

ordered number pair A pair of numbers used to locate points on a coordinate grid.

height of a prism The distance between the two opposite bases of a prism.

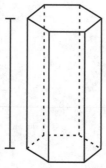

volume A measure of the amount of space taken up by a 3-dimensional object.

square centimeter (square cm, cm²) A unit for measuring area.

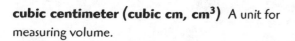

cubic centimeter (cubic cm, cm³) A unit for measuring volume.

weight The force of gravity pulling an object toward Earth or how heavy something is.

capacity of a scale The greatest weight a scale can measure. For example, most infant scales have a capacity of about 25 pounds.

capacity of a container The measure of how much liquid or other pourable substance a container will hold, or how much of a liquid or pourable substance there is.

frequency table A chart on which data are tallied to find the frequency of given events or values.

Waist-to-floor measurement (inches)	Frequency	
	Tallies	Number
27	//	2
28		0
29	ЖЖ	5
30	ЖЖ ///	8
31	ЖЖ //	7
32	////	4
		Total = 26

mode The number(s) or item(s) that occurs most often in a set of data. For example, in the frequency table above, 30 inches is the mode.

Use with Lesson 9.14.

Do-Anytime Activities

To work with your child on the concepts taught in this unit and in previous units, try these interesting and rewarding activities:

1 Review equivalent names for measurements. For example: *How many inches in 1 foot? How many pints in 3 quarts? How many centimeters in 1 meter? How many grams in 1 kilogram?*

2 Review multiplication facts. For example: *How much is 6 times 3? 7 × 8? 4 [5s]?*

3 Review division facts. For example: *How many 2s in 12? What number multiplied by 4 equals 12? How much is 18 divided by 2?*

4 Practice multiplication with multiples of 10, 100, and 1,000. For example: *How much are 10 [30s]? How much is 4 × 100? What number times 100 equals 4,000?*

5 Practice division with multiples of 10, 100, and 1,000. For example: *How much is $\frac{1}{10}$ of 300? How many 50s in 5,000? How much is 200 divided by 50?*

Building Skills through Games

In Unit 10, your child will practice mental-math skills by playing the following games:

Memory Addition/Subtraction

Partners agree on a target number. They take turns adding or subtracting any number from 1 to 5 into the memory of their calculators while keeping track of the sums or differences in their heads. Then they press the (MRC) key to see if the final memory sums match their initial target number.

Multiplication Top-It

Players turn over two cards and call out the product. The player with the higher product keeps all the cards. The player with more cards at the end wins! *You will receive more detailed directions for* Multiplication Top-It *when we begin to play it in class.*

As You Help Your Child with Homework

As your child brings home assignments, you may want to go over the instructions together, clarifying them as necessary. The answers listed below will guide you through this unit's Home Links.

Home Link 10.1

1. 60; 96

2. 9; 12; 17

3. 33; 6; 12

4. 2; 4; 6

5. $\frac{1}{2}$; $\frac{1}{320}$; $\frac{1}{8}$; $\frac{1}{4}$; $\frac{1}{2}$

6. 90; 152; 117

Home Link 10.3

1. 100 cubic cm

2. 8 square cm

3. 100 square cm; 400 cubic cm

4. 52 square cm

5. 260 cubic cm

Home Link 10.6

1. inch

2. gram

3. square yard

4. centimeter

5. inch

6. quart

7. liter

8. 20 minutes

Home Link 10.7

4. 3

Home Link 10.8

1. 56.3

2. 12.8

Home Link 10.9

1. $20 \times 30 = 600$
$30 \times 20 = 600$
$600 \div 30 = 20$
$600 \div 20 = 30$

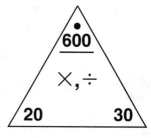

2. $40 \times 20 = 800$
$20 \times 40 = 800$
$800 \div 40 = 20$
$800 \div 20 = 40$

3. $100 \times 5 = 500$
$5 \times 100 = 100$
$500 \div 100 = 5$
$500 \div 5 = 100$

4. $600 \times 7 = 4,200$
$7 \times 600 = 4,200$
$4,200 \div 600 = 7$
$4,200 \div 7 = 600$

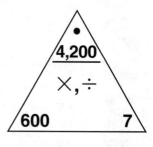

Home Link 10.11

(3,6) Algeria   (4,3) Zaire   (5,5) Sudan

(4,5) Chad   (5,6) Egypt   (4,6) Libya

Use with Lesson 9.14.

Old-Fashion Equivalencies

Family Note

Here is a page from a third grade math book published in 1897. These are the kinds of measurement problems children were expected to do over 100 years ago. The rod is a unit that is not often used today. It was used to measure land.

Please return this Home Link to school tomorrow.

Solve the problems yourself. Write your answers on the "slate."

12 inches (in.) = 1 foot (ft.)

   3 feet   = 1 yard (yd.)

$16\frac{1}{2}$ feet   = 1 rod (rd.)

$5\frac{1}{2}$ yards   = 1 rod

320 rods   = 1 mile (mi.)

1. How many inches are there in 5 ft.? in 8 ft.?

2. How many yards are there in 27 ft.? in 36 ft.? in 51 ft.?

3. How many feet are there in 2 rd.? in 2 yd.? in 4 yd.?

4. How many rods are there in 33 ft.? in 66 ft.? in 99 ft.?

5. What part of a yard is $1\frac{1}{2}$ ft.? What part of a mile is 1 rd.? 40 rd.? 80 rd.? 160 rd.?

6. How many inches are there in $7\frac{1}{2}$ ft.? in $12\frac{2}{3}$ ft.? in $9\frac{3}{4}$ ft.?

Graded Work in Arithmetic: Third Year by S.W. Baird, 1897.

1. _____ _____

2. _____

   _____

3. _____ _____

   _____

4. _____ _____

   _____

5. _____

   ____ ____ ____ ____

6. _____ _____

   _____

Exploring the Volume of Boxes

Family Note

To explore the concept of volume, our class built open boxes out of patterns like the ones in this Home Link and then filled the boxes with centimeter cubes. Your child should try to calculate the volume of the boxes he or she builds on this Home Link by imagining that it is filled with cubes. Then have your child check the results by pouring a substance from one box to the other, as described below.

Please return this Home Link to school tomorrow.

1. Cut out the patterns. Tape or glue each pattern to make an open box. Find 2 boxes that have the same volume.

2. How did you figure out your answer?

_____

_____

_____

_____

_____

_____

_____

_____

_____

3. Check your answer by pouring rice, dried beans, or sand into one of the boxes. Fill the box to the top and level it off with a straightedge like an index card or a ruler. Then pour it into another box. Explain what happens if the boxes have the same volume.

_____

_____

_____

Exploring the Volume of Boxes (cont.)

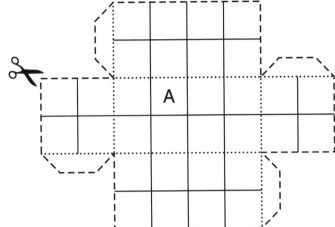

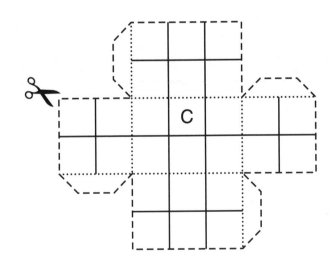

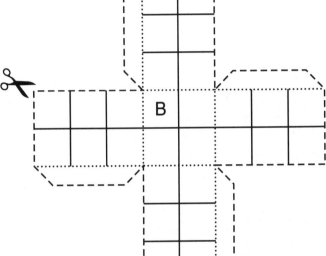

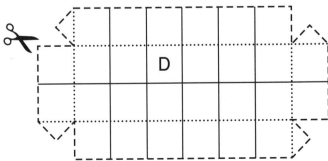

Name   Date   Time

Volumes of Rectangular Prisms

Family Note

Our class continues to use centimeter cubes and other base–10 blocks to explore the volume of rectangular prisms. It is helpful to think of the volume as a certain number of layers of cubes, where each layer has the same number of cubes.

Please return this Home Link to school tomorrow.

Jerry built a rectangular prism out of base-10 blocks.

1. First he used 25 cm cubes to make the base. He put
    3 more layers of cubes on top of the first layer of cubes.
    What is the volume of the prism he built?   _____ cubic cm

2. Next he used 48 cm cubes to make another prism. He
    made it with 6 layers of cubes. What is the area of the
    base of the prism?   _____ square cm

3. For his next prism, he used 1 flat for the base.
    He put 3 more flats on top of the base.
    What is the area of the base?   _____ square cm

    What is the volume of the prism?   _____ cubic cm

4. For his last prism, he used 4 longs and 12 cm cubes for
    the base. Draw a picture of the base on the grid below.
    What is the area of the base?   _____ square cm

5. He added 4 more layers of base-10 blocks on top of
    the base. What is the volume of the prism?   _____ cubic cm

Scales for Weighing

Family Note

Help your child use any scales you have (such as a bath scale or a postal scale) to weigh objects. Find the weights in U.S. customary units (such as ounces and pounds) or in metric units (such as grams and kilograms), or both.

Please return this Home Link to school tomorrow.

Ask someone at home to let you use one or more weighing scales. Weigh many different things and record their weights below. If possible, weigh them in both U.S. customary and metric units. Be sure to write the unit for each weight.

If you have only a bath scale, you can estimate the weight of light objects. First, weigh yourself holding the object. Weigh yourself again *not* holding the object. Then find the difference between the two weights.

Object	U.S. Customary Weight	Metric Weight

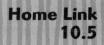

Family Note

Today, our class measured the weight and volume of several objects. We tried to decide whether an object that weighs more than another object always has the greater volume. Ask your child, "Which takes up more space, a pound of popped popcorn or a pound of marbles?"

Please return this Home Link to school tomorrow.

A. Ask someone at home to help you find food containers showing nutritional information. For example, you might look on canned goods, cereal boxes, bags of cookies, or bottles of cooking oil. Bring the labels or empty containers to school. Be sure they are clean.

B. Play a game of *Multiplication Top-It* with 1 or 2 people at home. *Multiplication Top-It* is similar to the card game *War.*

Directions

1. Remove the face cards from a regular deck of cards. The aces are the 1-cards.

2. Shuffle the cards. Place the deck facedown on the table.

3. Each player turns over two cards and calls out the product of the numbers. The player with the higher product wins the round and takes all the cards.

4. In case of a tie, each player turns over two more cards and calls out the product. The player with the higher product then takes all the cards from both plays.

5. Play ends when not enough cards are left for both players to turn over two cards. The player with more cards wins.

Example Ann turns over a 6 and a 2. She calls out 12.
Joe turns over a 10 and a 4. He calls out 40.
Joe has the higher product. He takes all 4 cards.

Matching Units of Measure

Family Note

Today our class explored units of capacity—cups, pints, quarts, gallons, milliliters, and liters. For the list below, your child should choose an appropriate unit for measuring each item. Some of the items refer to capacity, but units of length, weight, area, and volume are also included. Do not expect your child to know all of the units. Remind your child that *square units* refer to area measurement and *cubic units* to volume measurements.

Please return this Home Link to school tomorrow.

Fill in the oval to mark the unit you would use to measure each object.

Object	Units		
1. height of a chair	O meter	O inch	O pound
2. weight of a penny	O pound	O inch	O gram
3. area of a football field	O square inch	O square yard	O cubic meter
4. perimeter of your journal	O kilometer	O gallon	O centimeter
5. diameter of a dinner plate	O foot	O cubic centimeter	O inch
6. amount of juice in a carton	O meter	O quart	O square liter

7. About how much water could you drink in 1 day?

O 1 cup   O 1 milliliter   O 1 liter   O 1 gallon

Challenge

8. About how long would it take you to walk 1 mile? Then explain.

O 5 minutes   O 5 seconds   O 20 minutes   O 1 day

_____

_____

Mean (or Average) Number of Fish

Family Note

Many of us learned that to find the mean (or average) of a set of numbers, we add all the numbers and then divide the total by how many numbers we added. In today's lesson, the class tried a different method of finding the mean. After your child has completed the page, ask him or her to explain how this method works. In the next lesson, we will introduce finding the mean by adding the numbers and dividing to find the answer.

Please return this Home Link to school tomorrow.

The table below lists how many goldfish each child won at the school fun fair.

Name	Number of Goldfish
Reba	3
Bill	1
Lucy	7
Meg	0
Nate	5
Pat	2

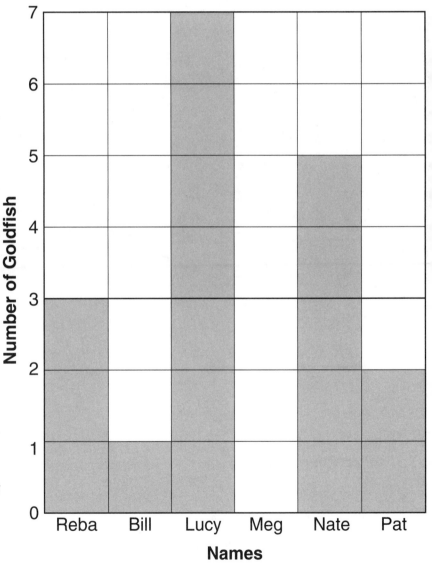

1. Put a penny over each shaded square in the bar graph.

2. Move the pennies so that each column has the same number of pennies.

3. Draw a horizontal line across your graph to show the height of the pennies when all of the columns are the same height.

4. The mean (or average) number of goldfish won by children at the fun fair is _____.

Finding the Mean

Family Note

The median and mean (or average) indicate "typical" values in a set of data. The median is the middle value when the data numbers are listed in order. The mean (or average) is found by the process described below. Your child may use a calculator to solve the problems. (In third grade, we ignore any digits to the right of the tenths place.)

Please return this Home Link to school tomorrow.

To find the mean (or average):	**Example**
	Basketball Scores: 80, 85, 76
1. Find the sum of the data numbers.	**1.** 80 + 85 + 76 = 241
2. Count the data numbers.	**2.** There are 3 scores.
3. Divide by the number of data numbers.	**3.** 241 ÷ 3 = 80.333333...
4. Drop any digits after tenths.	**4.** Mean: 80.3

Baseball Home Run Leaders

1994	Matt Williams	43
1995	Albert Belle	50
1996	Mark McGwire	52
1997	Mark McGwire	58
1998	Mark McGwire	70
1999	Mark McGwire	65

1. Mean number of home runs: _____

Baseball Home Run Leaders

1901	Sam Crawford	16
1902	Socks Seybold	16
1903	Buck Freeman	13
1904	Harry Davis	10
1905	Fred Odwell	9

2. Mean number of home runs: _____

Source: World Almanac, 1999

3. List some data for people in your home—for example, their ages, shoe sizes, or heights. Find the median and mean of the data.

Kind of data _____

Data _____

Median: _____   Mean: _____

Fact Triangles

Family Note

In today's lesson, we learned about the memory keys on our calculators. If you have a calculator, ask your child to show you how to store a number in the calculator's memory. If your calculator is different from the ones we use in class, you might need to help your child figure out how to use it.

Please return this Home Link to school tomorrow.

Fill in the missing number in each Fact Triangle. Then write the fact families for the three numbers in the Fact Triangles.

1.

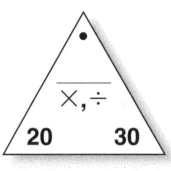

_____
_____
_____
_____

2.

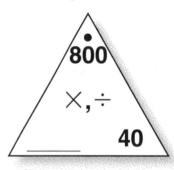

_____
_____
_____
_____

3.

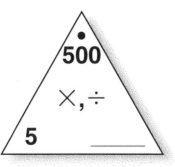

_____
_____
_____
_____

4.

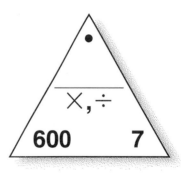

_____
_____
_____
_____

A Frequency Table

Family Note

Today we learned how to organize data in a frequency table. For today's Home Link, help your child count the number of electrical outlets in at least 8 different rooms. It would be best if the rooms were all in the same kind of building—for example, rooms in a house or apartment; rooms in the local library; or rooms in a school.

Please return this Home Link to school tomorrow.

1. Make a frequency table for the number of electrical outlets in at least 8 different rooms.

Number of Electrical Outlets

Room	Frequency	
	Tallies	**Number**

2. What is the *median* (middle) number of outlets? _____

3. What is the *mean* (or average) number of outlets? (You may use a calculator to calculate the answer. Drop any digits to the right of the tenths place.) _____

4. What is the *mode* of the data in the table? (*Reminder:* The mode is the number that occurs most often in a set of data.) _____

Locating Points on a Map

Family Note

In an ordered pair, such as (3,6), the first number indicates how far the point is to the right (or left) of 0. The second number indicates how far it is above (or below) 0.

Please return this Home Link to school tomorrow.

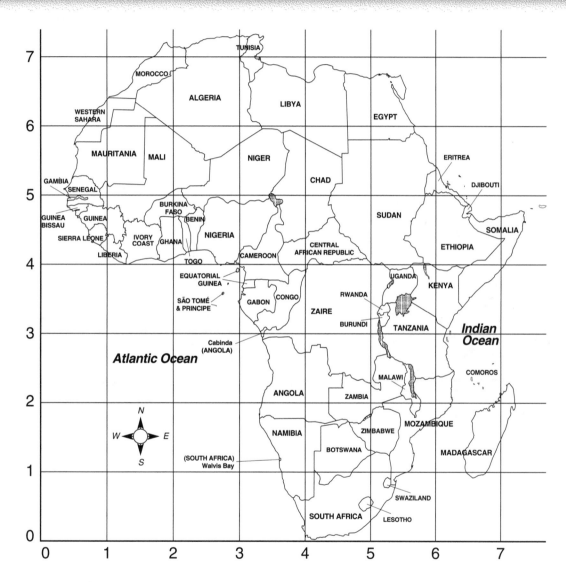

Here is a map of Africa. Write the name of the country in which each point is located.

1. (3,6) _____ **2.** (4,3) _____ **3.** (5,5) _____

4. (4,5) _____ **5.** (5,6) _____ **6.** (4,6) _____

Family Letter

Unit 11: Probability; End-of-Year Review

Unit 11, this year's final unit, contains informal activities relating to chance and probability.

Some of these activities call for children to compare the likelihood of several possible outcomes of an event: Something is more likely to happen than is something else. For example, children will find which of the pattern blocks is most likely to land on an edge when tossed into the air.

Other activities ask children to estimate the chance that something will happen. For example, when a coin is tossed, the chance of it landing heads up is 1 out of 2.

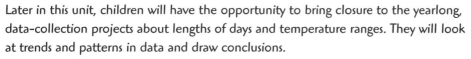

Later in this unit, children will have the opportunity to bring closure to the yearlong, data-collection projects about lengths of days and temperature ranges. They will look at trends and patterns in data and draw conclusions.

Please keep this Family Letter for reference as your child works through Unit 11.

Vocabulary

Important terms in Unit 11:

equally likely Each outcome has the same chance of occurring. For example, the possible outcomes of tossing a coin (HEADS or TAILS) are equally likely.

random draw Each item being drawn has the same chance of being selected. For example, children will draw blocks from a bag and realize that each block has an equal chance of being selected.

winter solstice The shortest day of the year; the first day of winter in the Northern Hemisphere. The winter solstice occurs on or about December 21.

summer solstice The longest day of the year; the first day of summer in the Northern Hemisphere. The summer solstice occurs on or about June 21.

Do-Anytime Activities

To work on the concepts taught in this unit and in previous units, try these interesting and rewarding activities:

1 When you are in the car or walking with your child, search for geometric figures. Identify them by name if possible and talk about their characteristics. For example, a stop sign is an octagon, which has 8 sides and 8 angles. A brick is a rectangular prism, in which all faces are rectangles.

2 Draw name-collection boxes for various numbers and together with your child write five to ten equivalent names in each box. Include name-collection boxes for fractions and decimals. For example, a $\frac{1}{2}$ name-collection box might include $\frac{2}{4}$, $\frac{10}{20}$, 0.5, 0.50, $\frac{500}{1,000}$, and so on. Then create name-collection boxes that included equivalent measures. For example, a 1 ft name-collection box might contain 12 in., $\frac{1}{3}$ yd, $\frac{1}{5,280}$ mile, $\frac{12}{36}$ yd, and so on.

1 ft
12 in. $\quad\quad \frac{1}{5,280}$ mile
$\frac{1}{3}$ yd $\quad\quad \frac{12}{36}$ yd

Use with Lesson 10.12.

Building Skills through Games

In Unit 11, your child will practice skills related to chance and probability by playing the following games. For detailed instructions, see the *Student Reference Book*.

The Block-Drawing Game

Without letting the other players see the blocks, a "Director" puts five blocks in a paper bag and tells the players how many blocks are in the bag. A player takes a block out of the bag. The "Director" records the color of the block for all players to see. The player replaces the block. At any time, a player may say "Stop!" and guess how many blocks of each color are in the bag.

Spinning to Win

Each player claims one section of the spinner—1, 2, 5, or 10. Players take turns spinning the spinner. If the spinner lands on a player's number, the player takes that number of pennies. The player with the most pennies after 12 spins wins the game.

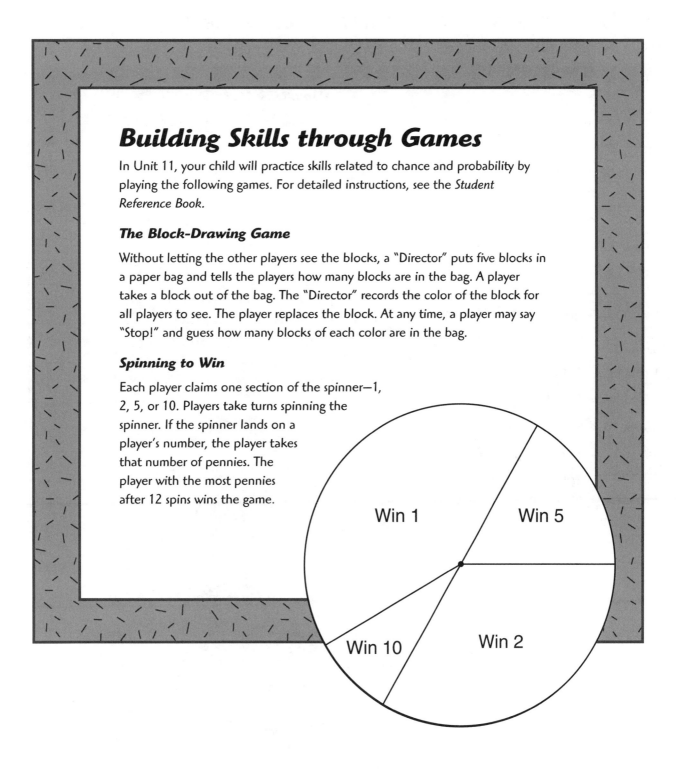

As You Help Your Child with Homework

As your child brings home assignments, you may want to go over the instructions together, clarifying them as necessary. The answers listed below will guide you through this unit's Home Links.

Home Link 11.1

1. sure to happen

2. sure not to happen

3. may happen, but not sure

4. may happen, but not sure

5. may happen, but not sure

Home Link 11.6

1. 0   **2.** 3   **3.** 6   **4.** 1

5. Sample answer: In Problem 3, $\frac{1}{4}$ of the blocks are blue; in Problem 4, $\frac{1}{4}$ of the blocks are red.

Home Link 11.7

1. 34 times   **2.** 57 times

3. 28 times   **4.** 18 times

Home Link 11.8

1. 13,841   **2.** 1,863   **3.** 2,075

4. 3,092   **5.** 6,865   **6.** 2,250

7. 2,709   **8.** 28,640   **9.** 7,200

Home Link 11.9

Numbers	Add	Subtract	Multiply	Divide
22 and 7	22 + 7 = 29	22 − 7 = 15	22 × 7 = 154	22 ÷ 7 → 3 R1
46 and 6	46 + 6 = 52	46 − 6 = 40	46 × 6 = 276	46 ÷ 6 → 7 R4
52 and 5	52 + 5 = 57	52 − 5 = 47	52 × 5 = 260	52 ÷ 5 → 10 R2
150 and 3	150 + 3 = 153	150 − 3 = 147	150 × 3 = 450	150 ÷ 3 = 50
560 and 80	560 + 80 = 640	560 − 80 = 480	560 × 80 = 44,800	560 ÷ 80 = 7
3,000 and 50	3,000 + 50 = 3,050	3,000 − 50 = 2,950	3,000 × 50 = 150,000	3,000 ÷ 50 = 60
12,000 and 60	12,000 + 60 = 12,060	12,000 − 60 = 11,940	12,000 × 60 = 720,000	12,000 ÷ 60 = 200

Likely and Unlikely Events

Family Note

During the next two weeks, please help your child find and cut out items in newspapers and magazines that discuss events that might or might not happen. Have your child bring these items to school to share with the class.

Please return this Home Link to school tomorrow.

For the next two weeks, look for items in newspapers and magazines that tell about events that might or might not happen. Get permission to cut them out and bring them to school. You might look for items like the following:

- a weather forecast (What are the chances that it will rain tomorrow?)
- the sports page (Which team is favored to win the baseball game?)
- a news story (What are the chances that people will explore distant planets in the next 20 years?)
- a health report (Are you more or less likely to catch a cold during the winter than during the summer?)

Tell whether each event below is "sure to happen," "sure not to happen," or "may happen, but not sure." Circle the answer.

1. You will grow taller next year.
   sure to happen   sure not to happen   may happen, but not sure

2. You will live to be 200 years old.
   sure to happen   sure not to happen   may happen, but not sure

3. You will receive a letter tomorrow.
   sure to happen   sure not to happen   may happen, but not sure

4. You will watch TV next Saturday.
   sure to happen   sure not to happen   may happen, but not sure

5. You will travel to the moon.
   sure to happen   sure not to happen   may happen, but not sure

Name   Date   Time

A Survey

Family Note

Have your child survey 10 people—family members, neighbors, and out-of-school friends—to find out how many are right-handed and how many are left-handed. Do not count people who say they are ambidextrous (people who are able to use both hands with equal ease). Take a few days to help your child complete the survey. The results won't be needed until Lesson 11.7.

1. Ask 10 people whether they are right-handed or left-handed. Do not ask people at your school. Do not count people who say they are neither right-handed nor left-handed. (People who don't prefer either hand are called *ambidextrous*.)

2. On the chart below, make a tally mark for each person. Be sure that you have exactly 10 marks.

3. When you have finished your survey, record the results at the bottom of the page. Bring the results to school.

	Tallies
Right-handed	
Left-handed	

✁ -

Name _____

Survey Results

Number of right-handed people: _____

Number of left-handed people: _____

Total: 10

A Fair Game?

Family Note

The class is exploring probability. Play the game *Scissors, Paper, Stone* with your child. After 20 rounds, have your child decide whether the game is fair and tell why or why not. (A game is "fair" if all players have an equal chance of winning or losing.)

Please return this Home Link to school tomorrow.

Play *Scissors, Paper, Stone* with someone at home. Play at least 20 times. Keep a tally of wins and losses.

Rules for *Scissors, Paper, Stone*

This is a game for 2 players. Players use their hands to represent a pair of scissors, a piece of paper, or a stone, as shown.

scissors   **paper**   **stone**

Each player hides one hand behind his or her back and puts it in the scissors, paper, or stone position.

One player counts, "One, two, three."
On "three," both players show their hands.
Who wins:

- Scissors cut paper. (If one player shows scissors and the other shows paper, scissors wins.)

- Paper covers stone. (If one player shows paper and the other shows stone, paper wins.)

- Stone dents scissors. (If one player shows stone and the other shows scissors, stone wins.)

- If both players show the same thing, no one wins.

1. Is this a fair game? (Fair means each player has the same chances.) _____

2. On the back of this paper, explain why or why not.

Based on rules for *Scissors, Paper, Stone* in *Family Fun and Games,* The Diagram Group, Sterling Publishing, 1992, p. 364

Another Fair Game?

Family Note

We continue to explore probability. Play the game *Fingers* with your child. After 20 games, have your child decide whether the game is fair and tell why or why not. (A game is "fair" if all players have an equal chance of winning or losing.)

Please return this Home Link to school tomorrow.

Play *Fingers* at least 20 times. Keep a tally of wins and losses.

Rules for *Fingers*

This is a game for 2 players. One player tries to guess the number of fingers the other player will "throw" (display).

1   2   3   4

You, the *Everyday Mathematics* student, can throw 1, 2, 3, or 4 fingers. The other player can throw only 1 or 2 fingers.

Players face each other. Each one puts a closed fist on his or her chest.

One player counts, "One, two, three." On "three," each player "throws" some number of fingers.

At the same time, both players call out what they think will be the total number of fingers thrown by both players.

- The player who calls out the correct total wins.
- If *neither* player calls out the correct total, no one wins.
- If *both* players call out the correct total, no one wins.

1. Is this game fair? (Fair means each player has the same chance of winning.) _____

2. On the back of this page explain why or why not.

Adaptation of rules for *Mora* in *Family Fun and Games,* The Diagram Group, Sterling Publishing, 1992, p. 365

Spinners

Family Note

We continue to study probability. Help your child design a spinner that meets the conditions in Part 1 below. Then help your child design another spinner by dividing the circle into parts ("wedges") and coloring the parts.

Please return this Home Link to school tomorrow.

Work with someone at home to make two spinners.

1. Use blue, red, yellow, and green crayons or coloring pencils on the first spinner. Color the spinner so that all of the following are true:

When spun around a pencil point in the center of the circle, a paper clip

- is very likely to land on red.
- has the same chance of landing on yellow as on green.
- may land on blue but is very unlikely to land on blue.

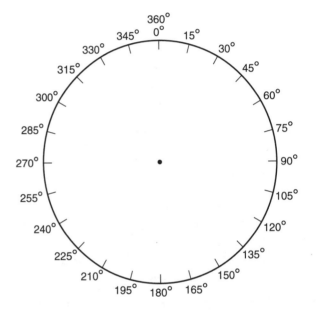

2. Design and color your own spinner. Then tell how likely or unlikely it is that the paper clip will land on each of the colors you used.

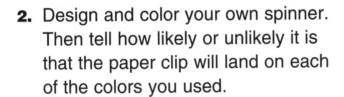

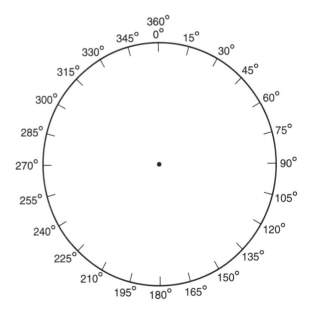

Drawing Blocks

Family Note

Have your child explain how to decide how many red blocks to put into each bag in the problems below. If you have time, do the block-drawing experiments with your child and record the results on the back of this page. Ask your child to explain how to do the experiments.

Please return this Home Link to school tomorrow.

Color the blocks in the bags blue.

Answer each question about how many red blocks to put into the bag.

Example: If I wanted to take out a blue block twice as often as a red block, I would put in 1 red block.

1. If I wanted to be sure to take out a blue block, I would put in _____ red block(s).

2. If I wanted to have an equal chance of taking out a red or blue block, I would put in _____ red block(s).

3. If I wanted to take out a red block about 3 times as often as a blue block, I would put in _____ red block(s).

4. If I want to take out a red block about $\frac{1}{4}$ of the time, I would put in _____ red block(s).

Challenge

5. How are Problems 3 and 4 alike?

_____

_____

More Random-Draw Problems

Home Link 11.7

Family Note

This Home Link focuses on predicting the contents of a jar by drawing out marbles. Don't expect your child to be an expert. Explorations with probability will continue through sixth grade. This is a first exposure.

Please return this Home Link to school tomorrow.

Each problem is about 10 marbles in a jar. The marbles are either black or white. Marbles are drawn randomly from the jar (without looking into the jar). The kind of marble drawn is tallied then returned to the jar.

- Decide, from the random draw, how many of each color there are.
- Shade the marbles in the jar to show your decision.

Example: From 100 random draws, you get:

a black marble ● 81 times

a white marble ○ 19 times

1. From 100 random draws, you get:

a black marble ● 34 times

a white marble ○ 66 times

2. From 100 random draws, you get:

a black marble ● 57 times

a white marble ○ 43 times

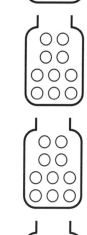

3. From 50 random draws, you get:

a black marble ● 28 times

a white marble ○ 22 times

Challenge

4. From 25 random draws, you get:

a black marble ● 18 times

a white marble ○ 7 times

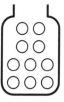

Multidigit Computation

Family Note

Your child should not use a calculator on these problems. This is a chance for you and your child to see which computation skills are solid and which require review.

Please return this Home Link to school tomorrow.

For each problem below, show your work and circle your answer.

1. 8,359 + 5,482	**2.** 3,641 − 1,778	**3.** 8,704 − 6,629
4. 12,550 − 9,458	**5.** 10,262 − 3,397	**6.** 250 × 9
7. 387 × 7	**8.** 716 × 40	**9.** 400 × 18